PREFACE

Here are two statements by physicists to introduce the material in this volume:

> Is it conceivable that a field theory permits one to understand the atomistic and quantum structure of reality? Almost everybody will answer this question with "no". But I believe that at the present time nobody knows anything reliable about it. This is so because we cannot judge in what manner and how strongly the exclusion of singularities reduces the manifold of solutions. We do not possess any method at all to derive systematically solutions that are free of singularities. Approximation methods are of no avail since one never knows whether or not there exists to a particular approximate solution an exact solution *free of singularities*. For this reason we cannot at present compare the content of a nonlinear field theory with experience. Only a significant progress in the mathematical methods can help here. At the present time the opinion prevails that a field theory must first, by "quantization", be transformed into a statistical theory of field probabilities according to more or less established rules. I see in this method only an attempt to describe relationships of an essentially nonlinear character by linear methods.

* * *

> Physicists have traditionally invented their own mathematics (Fourier, Gibbs, Heisenberg, Dirac). A major program of applying modern mathematics to physics gives one the feeling of a solution in search of a problem. From a physicist's perspective, the physics should come first and the mathematics should follow. I believe this is the course followed by even the most mathematical branches of theoretical physics such as axiomatic field theory or general relativity. Very modern mathematical tools have been applied to other specific problems, e.g., stability theory to mechanical systems, ergodic theory to statistical ones. In all cases, it has been the application of a powerful mathematical tool to a specific physics problem. Dr. Hermann mentions no real *specific* problems. All is very general.

These are the extremes of the physicist's attitude toward mathematics. Note particularly the machismo with which Physicist B claims to have "invented" everything. Obviously, my books are not for him; no doubt he will be proudly proclaiming in a few years that the physicists have "invented" differential geometry.

The main new material in this volume concerns old wine in new bottles. As I have been emphasizing in my work (*"Fourier Analysis on Groups and Partial Wave Analysis"*, *"Lie Algebras and Quantum Mechanics"*, *"Vector Bundles in Mathematical Physics"*, *"Geometry, Physics and Systems"*, and IM, Volumes 6 and 10), "gauge fields" are precisely what we call *connections*. Now, as mathematics, this subject was very well developed and understood when I became a graduate student in 1952. (In fact, it has really hardly advanced much since then.) Yet the only trace of this in the physics literature until 1967 (and it is only rather vague) is in a seminal and important paper, "Geometric Definitions of Gauge Invariance" by E. Lubkin in *Annals of Physics*, Volume 23, 1963, pages 233-283. The precise relation of the formalism of connection theory is not described there (nor are there any references to the mathematical literature of connection theory). Another historical curiosity is that C.N. Yang was a student of S.S. Chern precisely when Chern was doing his now famous work on connections and characteristic classes. When Yang and Mills did their work in the early 1950's, Chern's work was already famous.

My point in this book is that the "Yang-Mills" idea can be traced back even further to the Kaluza-Klein "unified field theory" of the early 1920's [1-3]. Of course, then it was a question of unifying gravitation and electromagnetics. The Yang-Mills fields are a direct generalization of the electromagnetic field and it should not be surprising that the Kaluza-Klein construction generalizes. The message of my work here is that it *does*, and that it involves precisely the notion of a connection on a principal fiber bundle. There are also implications for the "generalized Aharonov-Bohm" situation, recently considered by Wu and Yang [5].

Now, I believe that this association of Yang-Mills with Kaluza-Klein does more than establish historical continuity. The key geometric idea in Kaluza-Klein was to extend Einstein by constructing a *Riemannian metric*. It was considered then--and mathematicians still largely think this way--that Riemannian geometry was the only true geometric faith. Thus, writing down the laws of physics in terms of Riemannian geometry (particularly the "differential invariants" of the Riemannian metric, the *curvature*) was considered the highest form of poetry. Physicists have long played their own version of the Oedipal game and have rejected Einstein's esthetics, but I am beginning to think that the old boy might have been right after all. One of the main objections to Kaluza-Klein in the 1920's was the extra, fifth dimension that it involved. After fifty years of science fiction (and a lot more mathematics) we are a good deal more broad minded about such things. (The physicists call it "internal symmetry degrees of freedom", while we mathematicians can call it "principal fiber bundles over R^4 with compact Lie group as structure group" and make it seem more familiar.) Pushing the generality a bit further, I believe it is useful to invest a certain amount of effort to studying *Riemannian metrics on fiber spaces* whose base space is the space-time manifold of special or general relativity. This is my main theme.

I can think, off-the-cuff, of two major topics that need thorough thought and investigation. Dirac essentially used "connection-theoretic" ideas in his quantization of the unit of electric charge via the notion of magnetic monopole [5,6]. What is involved may be described as follows. Think of the electromagnetic field associated with a magnetic monopole as an $SO(2,R)$-principal bundle + (connection) with a non-simply-connected set R^4 minus a singularity subset as a base. $SO(2,R)$ has a unitary representation on $\mathbb{C}^1$. There will then be an associated *line bundle* or R^4 - (singularity subset). The cross-sections of this line bundle are identified with the Schrödinger wave function for the metric of an electron in this electromagnetic field. The electromagnetic field, as a connection, will define a *linear* connection for this vector bundle, *but with a parameter* λ related to the "charge" of the electron. The "geometric object" consisting of (line-bundle + connection) will have a *singularity* on the subset. For certain values of λ, something special will happen at this singularity. This will "quantize" λ ! Thought of in this geometric way, this is an enormously clever argument, and it is not clear if its full potentialities in elementary particle physics have ever been ascertained. (In my paper, "Analytical Continuation of Group Representations" [7], I was groping for some such picture of the way that "coupling constants" and "masses" could be "quantized".)

The other topic is *quantum mechanics* itself. As my faithful readers know, I am dubious that the standard quantum field theory-perturbation theory-renormalization theory is anything more than a rickety crutch which we can only dream of throwing away some day when the *real* Messiah comes. Geometrically, it suffers the fatal defect of being so horribly dependent on choice of coordinates, the choice of Hamiltonian as "free" and "interacting", etc. As I have already emphasized in my polemics in IM, Volume 12, Soliton Theory has shown us that the standard ideas are horribly incomplete, since they ignore the possibility of *new* phenomena arising in nonlinear situations which could far better elucidate elementary particles than the current monstrosity of theory.

Let us then say:

Yang-Mills = Kaluza-Klein = Riemannian geometry

= General Relativity .

How do we quantize? Of course, the attempt to quantize general relativity is as much a mess as anything else. I am convinced that we just have not thought of the right way to do it, or *what it means*. Dirac's monopole-quantization argument should be a clue. Another possibility might be to say: Given a Riemannian metric, construct the associated Laplace Beltrami (or Laplace-Dirac) differential operator. *Its* spectral properties should have something to do with quantization. (A major topic in global differential geometry these days is to correlate the geometric properties of elliptic Riemannian metrics on compact manifolds with the properties of the spectrum of the associated Laplace-Beltrami operator. I am thinking of something like that, but suitably specialized to the hyperbolic, non-compact situation.) Now that we understand better the geometry and analogies underlying the old "Bohr-Sommerfeld" quantization procedures, there are clearly other related possibilities that need to be investigated.

Although elementary particle physics is the field of science with the greatest intellectual appeal--and the closest relation to geometric mathematics--I believe that the main thrust of the field is completely distorted by the physicist's attitude toward mathematics. Particularly since the rise of "gauge theories" as a *crude* phenomonological guide to the interpretation of experiment (and they are so far no more than that) the subject has been waiting for the new Einstein to put together a suitable combination of intuitive physical insight and the "right" mathematical structure (and "right" includes all those classical elements of elegance, beauty, etc. that today's crop of physicists are completely untrained to understand, alas!) I believe the mathematical and physical ideas we need are lying at our feet. "Modern" differential geometry, *meaning* fiber bundles, connections, etc., is obviously the raw material.

Perhaps Einstein was not right in saying that quantum mechanics must be completely *replaced* by classical, nonlinear field-theoretic ideas. The quantum mechanical apparatus of Hilbert spaces, Hermitian operators, eigenvalues, etc. is obviously a very convenient and appealing way of making sense of the experimental data of elementary particle physics. (However, I worry about whether the experimentalists provide it in this way because the theorists tell them that is what they are supposed to do.) As a "compromise" let us say then that we must make more *compatible* the geometric and quantum mechanical world view. How to do this presents many fascinating mathematical problems, some of which I try to describe and develop here. Dirac's "quantization" of the monopole is obviously very significant as a mathematical model that could be much more extensively developed. It is also interesting to note that according to Lanczos' book, *The Einstein Decade*, Einstein was familiar with such things quite early and may be considered to be the precursor of the "geometric" W.K.B. theory developed by J. Keller and Maslow much later.

Obviously, the ideas of topological "global" differential geometry pose attractive supplementary possibilities to Einstein's basic program. Here one would throw in the names of John Wheeler and David Finkelstein as the most impressive thinkers along these lines. Wheeler's thoughts have gone toward the topology of space-time, Finkelstein's toward the topology of the "internal symmetry" space. (Finkelstein's recent work has tried to introduce a combinatorial-topological structure for space time which would be "compatible" with quantum mechanics. I have not yet been able to integrate Finkelstein's ideas into my world-view, partly because I love the continuum and the calculational tools we obtain from it and calculus. "Discrete" mathematics is actually much harder than "continuous".)

A point that is so difficult for physicists to understand is that developing these "fundamental" ideas is not a matter of doing a calculation using

Feynman diagrams, Clebsch-Gordan coefficients, etc. or even thinking up ingenious mechanisms to explain why other theoretical ideas (e.g., quarks) do not produce the desired experimental consequences! Thus anyone with any feeling for classical science would look with extreme suspicion at the whole gerrymandered business--quarks, supersymmetries, bags, strings, chains,... and all. Perhaps a period of extreme Puritan austerity and simplicity is needed--no more Nobel prizes for last year's fad, calls to the *New York Times*, feverish articles in *Scientific American*, etc.

Elementary particle physicists are most excited now by "gauge theories", particularly something called "quantum chromodynamics". This is a Lagrangian quantum field theory which is admirable for certain phenomenological purposes. (It basically consists of "quark fields" with "Yang-Mills fields" tying them together.) I am extremely skeptical that we know enough to deduce anything very lasting from these models. They have two basic mathematical features that are very badly understood--a "degenerate" vacuum, and an infinite dimensional Lie symmetry group. The physicists use these additional degrees of freedom for ingenious phenomenological purposes, but have never come to grips with the mathematical reality. (For example, in classical field theories the "ground states" are the minimum of energy. In the usual field theories, these are calculus of variations problems involving three independent variables; mathematicians know that there is a whole zoo of possible pathologies--solutions with horns, spikes, etc.) The recent work on "instantons" is an ingenious attempt to get around this, or give it a satisfactory physical interpretation, but here I am dubious that a field theory involving *elliptic* differential equations can say very much about our Minkowski-hyperbolic world. However, the work of Atiyah, Singer, and Ward on these gadgets is mathematically interesting, and might be the camel's nose under the tent for the use of more sophisticated geometric methods in elementary particle physics.

My main interest is the possible relation between the work on prolongations-Bäcklund-solitons (described in "Interdisciplinary Mathematics", Volumes 12, 14, 15, 18, and "Lie Groups", Volume 6) and instantons. Certainly both involve connection theory in an extraordinarily intimate way! Thus it has been encouraging to see a recent reprint "Bäcklund Transformations and the Construction of the Atiyah-Ward Ansatze for the Self-Dual SU(2) Gauge Fields" by Corrigan, Fairlie, Yates, and Goodard (DAMTP, Cambridge, England, #77(26)). (Although I do not understand it--too calculational!) The relation I see proceeds along the following general lines. (I follow the differential-geometric foundation for field theories described in *Lie Algebras and Quantum Mechanics*.) Let X be a suitable fiber bundle over the space-time manifold Y of dimension m. (Then, $m = 4$ for "our" world, $m = 2$ is all we know about as far as solitons are concerned.) Σ, the *state space* is a family of cross-section maps $\sigma: Y \to X$. Let $\mathcal{P}$ ("Poisson bracket algebra") be the space of pairs (α,V),

α = $(m-1)$-st degree differential form on X

V = vector field on X.

$$\alpha = V \lrcorner \Omega$$

where Ω is a closed $(m+1)$-form on X which *defines* the field theory. Make $\mathcal{P}$ into a Lie algebra by defining "Poisson bracket" as follows

$$\{(\alpha_1,V_1),(\alpha_2,V_2)\} = \left(\mathcal{L}_{V_1}(\alpha_2) - \mathcal{L}_{V_2}(\alpha_1),[V_1,V_2]\right)$$

($\mathcal{L}$ = Lie derivative. $[\ ,\ ]$ = Jacobi bracket.) Assign to each (α,V) the function

$$f_{(\alpha,V)}(\sigma) = \int_Z \sigma^*(\alpha) \quad .$$

where Z is an $(m-1)$-dimensional submanifold of Y. To define "soliton" (following Zabusky and Kruskal) we should be given a sequence

$$(\alpha_0, V_0), (\alpha_1, V_1), \ldots$$

of elements of $\mathscr{P}$ which are *in involution*, i.e., where Poisson brackets vanish. One then searches for the elements Σ which extremize

$$f_{(\alpha_n, V_n)},$$

with

$$f_{(\alpha_0, V_0)}, \ldots, f_{(\alpha_{n-1}, V_{n-1})}$$

held constant. These are the n-*solitons*. Now, what happens in Yang-Mills theories is that there are already *zero solitons*, i.e., "degenerate ground states". ($f_{(\alpha_0, V_0)}(\sigma)$ = "energy".) As I mentioned above, there has been very little serious work in these, especially quantum mechanically. The physicists make up fancy words to hide this fact, but at least the "instantons" are a reasonable suggestion. They are obtained as special solutions (with "singularities") of the *complexified* field equations which also satisfy (locally) the "zero energy" equations. (In Yang-Mills, they are the "self-dual" solutions.) The suggestion is that they "interpolate" or "tunnel between" the "degenerate ground states". (A recent review paper, "Quantum Meaning of Classical Field Theory" by R. Jackiw in *Rev. Mod. Phys.* is very illuminating here.)

It is not clear what to make of all this mathematically. (To my mind, they are very reminiscent of the "singular solutions" of 19-th century non-linear differential equation theory. As I emphasized in Volume 12, this provides many new perspectives on nonlinear field theories, of which physicists are now completely ignorant.) What I suspect is the real topic of interest is the study of "special", symmetry-related solutions of nonlinear field equations. After all, the only reason that Einstein's gravitational equations are at all useful as a guide to the physical world is the intricate structure that has been found in the Schwarzchild and other special solutions. If my insight is correct, we should also be looking for the equivalent of the "n-solitons", i.e., *other* conservation laws, involving *higher derivatives* in the fields. Certainly, this might be where the geometry of connections enters in a serious way.

Of course, I do not pretend to any great originality in this central vision of the close relation between connection-fiber bundle theory, quantization and elementary particles. In particular, I would like to draw attention to the work of Norman Hurt [8]. A soon-to-appear monograph by J. Sniatycki, "Geometric Quantization and Quantum Mechanics" will cover this material in greater detail, and no doubt will have many points in common.

I have divided the material in this volume into two categories--chapters and appendices. The former are approximations to what one would normally expect to see in a monograph, the latter are more fragmentary and tentative. Appendices D and E represent joint work with Estabrook and Wahlquist, to which I have attached their names (but I take all responsibility)

I am indebted to Roger Brockett and Shlomo Sternberg for suggestions and inspiration about this area. I would like to express my thanks to Karin Young and Hilda and Michael Bernstein for their great help in the MATH SCI PRESS enterprise.

Bibliography

1. E. Lubkin, Geometric definition of gauge invariance, Annals of Physics 23 (1963), 233-283.

2. T. Kaluza, Sitzunber. Preuss. Akad. Wiss. Phys. Math. Kl. (1921).

3. P.G. Bergmann, An Introduction to General Relativity, Prentice-Hall, 1942.

4. R.J. Torrence and W.M. Tultjyew, Gauge invariant canonical mechanics for charged particles, J. Math. Phys. 14 (1973), 1725-1732.

5. T.T. Wu and C.N. Yang, Phys. Rev. D 12 (1975), 3145.

6. P.A.M. Dirac, Proc. Roy. Soc. A133 (1931), 60.

7. R. Hermann, Analytic continuation of group representations, I-VI, Comm. Math. Phys. 2 (1966); 3 (1966), 53-97; 5 (1967), 131-190; 6 (1967), 205-225.

8. N. Hurt, Differential geometry of canonical quantization, Ann. Inst. Henri Poincaré, 14, 153-170.

TABLE OF CONTENTS

Page

Page

Chapter I

YANG-MILLS, KALUZA-KLEIN AND RIEMANNIAN SUBMERSIONS WITH TOTALLY GEODESIC FIBERS

1. INTRODUCTION

The Yang-Mills equations are one of the primary objects of interest in elementary particle physics these days. They are, of course, intimately tied to differential geometric ideas, since they are nothing but special types of connections--in the sense developed by E. Cartan and C. Ehresmann [1,2]--for certain types of fiber bundles with compact Lie groups as structure group.

Thus, the question of the physical meaning of these bundles and connections presents itself. Now, in the special case that the structure group is abelian and one-dimensional, the Yang-Mills equations reduce to Maxwell's. The Kaluza-Klein "unified field theory" is one of the more plausible ways to "geometrize" the electromagnetic field. What I shall do here is to recast the classical Kaluza-Klein theory in terms of "modern" differential geometry, emphasizing the more recent theory of Riemannian submersions, due to B. Reinhart, the author, and B. O'Neill [4,5,37,47]. (In Interdisciplinary Mathematics, Volumes 5 and 10 this is recast in a form better suited to relativistic physics.) Then, we shall be in a good position to generalize to the Yang-Mills situation.

I would like to thank Shlomo Sternberg for several conversations about the general geometry of the Yang-Mills situation. He is pursuing an alternate direction in the search for a geometric intepretation of the fascinating Yang-Mills object [49]. I also thank Roger Brockett for stimulating conversations. It was his suggestion that led me to this Kaluza-Klein point of view.

2. GENERAL DIFFERENTIAL-GEOMETRIC NOTATION AND IDEAS

"Manifolds" will be finite dimensional, C^∞ and paracompact (i.e., the union of a countable number of compact subsets). Of course, most of the ideas generalize to other contexts. Maps, tensor fields, etc. will be of differentiability class C^∞, unless mentioned otherwise.

Let X be a manifold. $\mathscr{F}(X)$ denotes the algebra of C^∞, real-valued functions on X. $\mathscr{F}(X)$ is the basic "object" from which all other differential-geometric objects are constructed by methodical algebraic operations. (See IM, Volumes 16 and 17 for the foundations of differential geometry based in this way on manifold theory.)

A *vector field* on X is an R-linear map $V: \mathscr{F}(X) \to \mathscr{F}(X)$ which is a *derivation* of the algebra structure, i.e.,

$$V(f_1 f_2) = V(f_1) f_2 + f_1 V(f_2) \quad ,$$

for $f_1, f_2 \in \mathscr{F}(X)$. $\mathscr{V}(X)$ denotes the set of vector fields. Elements of $V \in \mathscr{V}(X)$ can be multiplied by functions, and two of them, V_1, V_2 can be composed as the *Jacobi bracket*

$$(V_1, V_2) \to [V_1, V_2] = V_1 V_2 - V_2 V_1 \quad .$$

$\mathscr{V}(X)$ in this way becomes both an $\mathscr{F}(X)$*-module* and a *real Lie algebra.*

A vector field $V \in \mathscr{V}(X)$ is said to *vanish at a point* $x \in X$ if

$$V(f)(x) = 0$$

$$\text{for all } f \in \mathscr{F}(X) \quad .$$

Let X_x denote the vector space which is the quotient vector space of $\mathscr{V}(X)$ by the linear subspace of those V's which vanish at x. One can assign to each $v \in X_x$ a linear map

$$\mathscr{F}(X) \to R$$

as follows:

$$v(f) = V(f)(x) \quad ,$$

where V is any element in $\mathscr{V}(X)$ whose image is v.

$$X_x \equiv \mathscr{V}(X)/(\quad) \quad .$$

This linear map satisfies:

$$v(f_1 f_2) = v(f_1) f_2(x) + f_1(x) v(f_2) \tag{2.1}$$

$$\text{for } f_1, f_2 \in \mathscr{F}(X) \quad .$$

(This is the "directional derivative" condition.) One can prove, conversely, that X_x is identified with the set of linear maps $v\colon \mathscr{F}(X) \to R$ satisfying condition (2.1). X_x is called the *tangent space to* X *at* x. (The "directional derivative" method is in fact the more usual one in foundational treatments, following Chevalley's book, Lie Groups, which is the original source for the methodology of modern differential geometry.)

The *tangent bundle* to X, denoted as T(X), is defined as follows: A "point" of T(X) is a pair (v,x) with $v \in X_x$. (v,x) is "projected" into x to define a map $T(X) \to X$ which makes T(X) into a *vector bundle* over X (i.e., the fibers are vector spaces.)

A *one-differential form* on X is an element of the dual space of $\mathscr{V}(X)$ *as an* $\mathscr{F}(X)$*-module*, i.e., an R-linear map

$$\theta\colon \mathscr{V}(X) \to \mathscr{F}(X)$$

such that

$$\theta(fV) = f\theta(V)$$

for $f \in \mathscr{F}(X)$, $V \in \mathscr{V}(X)$.

The collection of such forms, i.e., the $\mathscr{F}(X)$-dual of $\mathscr{V}(X)$, is denoted as $\mathscr{D}^1(X)$. For notational purposes it is often convenient to identify $\mathscr{D}^0(X)$ with $\mathscr{F}(X)$, i.e., to regard a zero-th degree differential form as a function (or a "scalar field" in tensor analysis language. A vector field is a "one-contravariant" tensor field, while a one-differential form is a "one-covariant" tensor field.) An r-*differential form* is an $\mathscr{F}(X)$-multilinear map

$$\omega: \underbrace{\mathscr{V}(X) \times \cdots \times \mathscr{V}(X)}_{\text{r copies}} \to \mathscr{F}(X) .$$

They are denoted as $\mathscr{D}^r(X)$.

The "natural" operations of differential calculus on manifolds are:

a) Jacobi bracket

$$(V_1,V_2) \to [V_1,V_2]$$

on vector fields

b) Exterior derivative

$$d: \mathscr{D}^r(X) \to \mathscr{D}^{r+1}(X) \quad , \quad r = 0,1,2,\ldots \quad .$$

c) Lie derivative, $(V,\omega) \to \mathscr{L}_V(\omega)$, mapping $\mathscr{V}(X) \times \mathscr{D}^r(X) \to \mathscr{D}^r(X)$.

In addition, there are:

d) Exterior multiplication

$$\wedge: \mathscr{D}^r(X) \times \mathscr{D}^s(X) \to \mathscr{D}^{r+s}(X)$$

e) Contraction

$$(V,\omega) \to V \lrcorner \omega \quad ,$$

mapping $\mathscr{V}(X) \times \mathscr{D}^r(X) \to \mathscr{D}^{r-1}(X)$

All of this has been "statically" considered on a single space X. The "naturality" or "covariance" of these objects and operations become apparent when maps $\phi: X \to Y$ between manifolds are considered:

$$\phi^* : \mathcal{F}(Y) \to \mathcal{F}(X)$$

is the dual map on functions determined via the formula

$$\phi^*(f)(x) = f(\phi(x)) \quad,$$

or the commutative mapping diagram

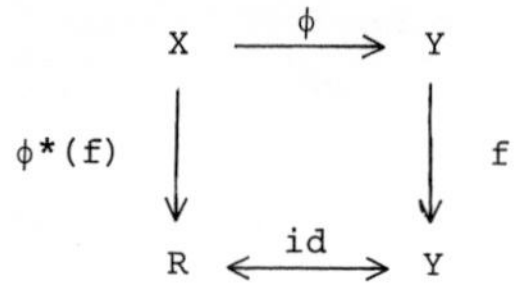

ϕ^* extends to a map: $\mathcal{D}^r(Y) \to \mathcal{D}^r(X)$, such that

$$\phi^*(d\omega) = d\phi^*(\omega)$$

$$\phi^*(\omega_1 \wedge \omega_2) = \phi^*(\omega_1) \wedge \phi^*(\omega_2) \quad.$$

For each $x \in X$,

$$\phi_* : X_x \to Y_{\phi(x)} \quad,$$

the *induced map on tangent vectors*, is defined as:

$$\phi_*(v)(f) = v(\phi^*(f)) \quad.$$

ϕ_* defines a linear vector bundle map $T(X) \to T(Y)$, leading to a commutative diagram

$$
\begin{array}{ccc}
T(X) & \xrightarrow{\ \phi_* \ } & T(Y) \\
\downarrow & & \downarrow \\
X & \xrightarrow{\ \phi \ } & Y
\end{array}
$$

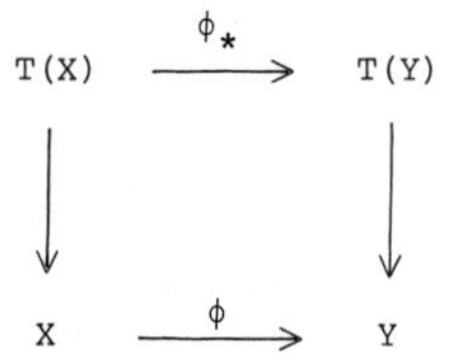

With this general notation in hand (all of which we shall not need, at least for the moment), let us turn to the Kaluza-Klein theory.

3. THE KALUZA-KLEIN GEOMETRIC THEORY OF THE ELECTROMAGNETIC FIELD

Let X be R^4, considered as the space-time manifold of special relativity. Let Cartesian coordinates on R^4 be denoted as x^μ, $0 \le \mu, \nu \le 3$. Then

$$x^0 = t = \text{physical "time" coordinate} \quad,$$

$$\vec{x} = (x^1, x^2, x^3) = \text{"space" coordinates.}$$

Let

$$\theta = A_\mu \, dx^\mu$$

be a one-differential form on X. Its components are the *electromagnetic field potentials*. (See [50] for the standard physics of electromagnetism.)

Let T(X) be the tangent bundle to X. We can consider the coordinate system of T(X) as

$$(x^\mu, \dot{x}^\mu)$$

The x^μ are the pull-backs to T(X) of the x^μ, with no change in notation.

$$\dot{x}^\mu(v) = v(x^\mu)$$

for $v \in T(X)$.

Let

$$L: T(X) \to R$$

be the function defined as follows:

$$L = (g_{\mu\nu}\dot{x}^\mu \dot{x}^\nu)^{1/2} + \frac{e}{mc^2} A_\mu \dot{x}^\mu \qquad (3.1)$$

It defines a calculus of variations problem for X. e and m are constants, the *charge* and *mass* of the charged particle. $g_{\mu\nu}$ is the metric tensor of Minkowski space, i.e.,

$$g_{ij} = -\delta_{ij} \; ; \qquad g_{00} = c^2 \; ; \qquad g_{0i} = 0 \; .$$

Then,

$$\frac{\partial L}{\partial \dot{x}^\mu} = \frac{g_{\mu\nu}\dot{x}^\nu}{(g\dot{x}\dot{x})^{1/2}} + \frac{e}{mc^2} A_\mu$$

In computing the extremals of the calculus of variations problem defined by L, i.e., the extremals of

$$\int L\left(x, \frac{dx}{dt}\right) ds \qquad ,$$

assume (as we may, without loss in generality, since the Lagrangian is homogeneous of degree +1 in $\dot{x}$) that:

$$g\dot{x}\dot{x} = \text{constant} \quad .$$

Thus, the extremal equations are

$$\frac{\frac{d}{ds}(g_{\mu\nu}\dot{x}^{\nu})}{(g\dot{x}\dot{x})^{1/2}} + \frac{e}{mc^2}\frac{\partial}{\partial x^{\nu}}(A_{\mu})\dot{x}^{\nu} = \frac{\partial L}{\partial x^{\mu}}$$

$$= \frac{e}{mc^2}\frac{\partial A_{\nu}}{\partial x^{\mu}}\dot{x}^{\nu}$$

or

$$\frac{\frac{d}{ds}(g_{\mu\nu}\dot{x}^{\nu})}{(g\dot{x}\dot{x})^{1/2}} = \frac{e}{mc^2}F_{\mu\nu}\dot{x}^{\nu} \quad , \tag{3.2}$$

with

$$\frac{1}{2}F_{\mu\nu} = \frac{\partial A_{\nu}}{\partial x^{\mu}} - \frac{\partial A_{\mu}}{\partial x^{\nu}} \tag{3.3}$$

$F_{\mu\nu}$ is, of course, the *electromagnetic field.*

$$2F_{\mu\nu}dx^{\mu} \wedge dx^{\nu} = 2d(A_{\nu}dx^{\nu})$$

$$= 2d\theta \quad .$$

This is, of course, the very familiar set of equations for the motion of a charged particle in an electromagnetic field.

Now, let Y be a *five*-dimensional manifold with coordinates labelled

$$(x^{\mu},\phi) \quad . \tag{3.4}$$

Let $\pi: Y \to X$ be the map such that

$$\pi^*(x^{\mu}) = x^{\mu} \quad ,$$

i.e., π is (locally) the projection of $R^5 \to R^4$. (In the "global" translation, π will be a fiber bundle with $SO(2,R)$ as structure group, and compact, one-dimensional fiber.) Now set:

$$L' = \frac{1}{2}g_{\mu\nu}\dot{x}^{\mu}\dot{x}^{\nu} + (\dot{\phi} - A_{\mu}\dot{x}^{\mu})^2 \quad . \tag{3.5}$$

Let us regard L' as a function on T(Y), hence as defining a calculus-of-variations problem with Y as configuration space. In fact, notice that *its extremals are geodesics of a Riemannian metric on* Y. This should be regarded as more geometrically "natural"--and certainly much more in the Einsteinian program of deriving physical "laws" from natural geometric structures. Let us now compute its extremals:

$$\begin{aligned}
\frac{\partial L'}{\partial \dot{x}^{\mu}} &= g_{\mu\nu}\dot{x}^{\nu} - 2(\dot{\phi} - A\dot{x})A_{\mu} \\
\frac{\partial L'}{\partial \dot{\phi}} &= 2(\dot{\phi} - A\dot{x}) \\
\frac{\partial L'}{\partial x^{\mu}} &= 2(\dot{\phi} - A\dot{x})\frac{\partial A_{\nu}}{\partial x^{\mu}}\dot{x}^{\nu} \\
\frac{\partial L'}{\partial \phi} &= 0 \quad .
\end{aligned} \tag{3.6}$$

Lagrange's equations for this Lagrangian now imply that

$$\frac{d}{ds}\left(\frac{\partial L'}{\partial \dot{\phi}}\right) = 0 \quad ,$$

i.e.,

$$\dot{\phi} - A_{\mu}\dot{x}^{\mu} = a \equiv \text{constant along the extremal} \tag{3.7}$$

Thus, the rest of Lagrange's equations take the form:

$$\frac{d}{ds}(g_{\mu\nu}\dot{x}^{\nu}) - 2a\frac{\partial A_{\mu}}{\partial x^{\nu}}\dot{x}^{\nu} = 2a\frac{\partial A_{\nu}}{\partial x^{\mu}}\dot{x}^{\mu}$$

or

$$\frac{d}{ds}(g_{\mu\nu}\dot{x}^{\nu}) = 2aF_{\mu\nu}\dot{x}^{\nu} \tag{3.8}$$

We may sum up as follows:

Theorem 3.1. The Lagrangian L' on Y for which a takes a suitable value has the property that its extremal curves project under π into the extremal curves of L. Thus, the class of all charged particle trajectories--with varying values of e/m --is "parameterized" by the set of all extremals of L', i.e., by the *geodesics of a Riemannian metric on* Y.

This Riemannian metric, which we call the *Kaluza-Klein metric*, is a natural geometric object attached to the electromagnetic field. The "charge"

e is, in a sense, parameterized by "ϕ", the fiber of the fiber space Y when considered as a fiber bundle over $X = R^4$. We will see later on that this generalizes *in a natural way* to Yang-Mills fields. Notice that there are potentialities for "quantization"-- ϕ is interpreted as a fiber on the circle S^1 acted on by $SO(2,R)$; "charge" is then "quantized" via the irreducible unitary representations of $SO(2,R)$.

4. THE CURVATURE OF THE KALUZA-KLEIN METRIC. MAXWELL'S EQUATIONS IN TERMS OF THE RICCI CURVATURE

As we have seen, the Kaluza-Klein electromagnetic theory is geometrically more natural and interesting from a differential geometric point of view since it involves a *Riemannian metric*, rather than (as in the standard Einstein-Maxwell theory) a pair of objects, i.e., a metric and a one-form. Of course, this "naturality" is purchased at the expense of a higher dimensional space.

Whenever a differential geometer sees a Riemannian metric, he likes to compute its curvature. I will now do this for Kaluza-Klein. I like to use Cartan's formalism for this, which works best if the metric is *elliptic* rather than hyperbolic. Hence, I will assume for the purposes of the calculation that the metric tensor is Euclidean, i.e.,

$$g_{\mu\nu} = \delta_{\mu\nu} \quad .$$

(The formulas can be "analytically continued".) The Riemannian metric Y is then

$$ds^2 = dx^\mu \cdot dx^\mu + (d\phi - \theta)\cdot(d\phi - \theta) \tag{4.1}$$

($\cdot$ denotes the *symmetric* tensor product of one-forms.) Thus, the

$$dx^\mu, \; d\phi - \theta \equiv d\phi - A_\mu dx^\mu$$

form an *orthonormal moving frame* for the metric.

The *Riemannian connection forms*

$$\omega^\mu_\nu = -\omega^\nu_\mu \quad , \quad \omega^4_\mu = -\omega^\mu_5$$

then satisfy the relations:

$$\begin{aligned} d(dx^\mu) &= 0 = \omega^\mu_\nu \wedge dx^\nu + \omega^\mu_4 \wedge (d\phi - \theta) \\ d(d\phi - \theta) &= -d\theta = \omega^4_\mu \wedge dx^\mu \end{aligned} \tag{4.2}$$

Thus,

$$(\omega^4_\mu - F_{\mu\nu}dx^\nu) \wedge dx^\mu = 0 \quad ,$$

or

$$\omega^4_\mu = F_{\mu\nu}dx^\nu = B_{\mu\nu}dx^\nu \tag{4.3}$$

with

$$B_{\mu\nu} = B_{\nu\mu} \quad .$$

Suppose then that

$$\omega^\mu_\nu = C^\mu_{\nu\omega}dx^\omega + C^\mu_{\nu 4}d\phi \tag{4.4}$$

Substitute (4.3) and (4.4) back into (4.2):

$$-\omega^4_\mu = \omega^\mu_4 = C^\mu_{\nu 4}dx^\nu \tag{4.5}$$

Compare (4.5) with (4.3), forcing

$$B_{\mu\nu} = 0$$

$$\omega^4_\mu = F_{\mu\nu}dx^\nu \tag{4.6}$$

Also,

$$C^\mu_{\nu\omega}dx^\omega \wedge dx^\mu = -F_{\mu\nu}dx^\nu \wedge A_\mu dx^\mu$$

$$C^\mu_{\nu\omega} - C^\mu_{\omega\nu} = F_{\mu\nu}A_\omega - F_{\mu\omega}A_\nu \tag{4.7}$$

Now, $C^\mu_{\nu\omega}$ is skew-symmetric in μ and ν. We can exploit this to compute it, with the aid of Formula (4.7). (This is the classic "Levi-Civita" calculation of the components of the affine connection associated with a Riemannian metric.)

$$\begin{aligned} C^\mu_{\nu\omega} &= C^\mu_{\omega\nu} + F_{\mu\nu}A_\omega - F_{\mu\omega}A_\nu - C^\omega_{\mu\nu} + F_{\mu\nu}A_\omega - F_{\mu\omega}A_\nu \\ &= -(C^\omega_{\nu\mu} + F_{\omega\mu}A_\nu - F_{\omega\nu}A_\mu) + F_{\mu\nu}A_\omega - F_{\mu\omega}A_\nu \\ &= C^\nu_{\omega\mu} + F_{\omega\nu}A_\mu + F_{\mu\nu}A_\omega \\ &= C^\nu_{\mu\omega} + F_{\nu\omega}A_\mu - F_{\nu\mu}A_\omega + F_{\omega\nu}A_\mu + F_{\mu\nu}A_\omega \end{aligned}$$

$$= - C^{\mu}_{\nu\omega} + 2F_{\mu\nu}A_{\omega} \quad ,$$

or

$$\boxed{C^{\mu}_{\nu\omega} = F_{\mu\nu}A_{\omega}} \tag{4.8}$$

Thus, we have:

$$\omega^{\mu}_{\nu} = F_{\mu\nu}A_{\omega}dx^{\omega} - F_{\mu\nu}d\phi$$

or

$$\boxed{\begin{aligned} \omega^{\nu}_{\mu} &= F_{\mu\nu}(d\phi - \theta) \\ \omega^{5}_{\mu} &= -\omega^{\mu}_{i} = F_{\mu\nu}dx^{\nu} \end{aligned}} \tag{4.9}$$

These formulas determine the connection forms associated with the Kaluza-Klein metric. The curvature forms are more readily calculated. Here is their definition

$$\boxed{\begin{aligned} \Omega^{\nu}_{\mu} &= d\omega^{\nu}_{\mu} - \omega^{\omega}_{\mu} \wedge \omega^{\nu}_{\omega} \\ \Omega^{4}_{\mu} &= d\omega^{4}_{\mu} - \omega^{\nu}_{\mu} \wedge \omega^{4}_{\nu} \end{aligned}} \tag{4.10}$$

Thus,

$$d\omega^{\nu}_{\mu} = F_{\mu\nu,\omega}dx^{\omega} \wedge (d\phi - \theta) - F_{\mu\nu}d\theta$$

$$\Omega^{\nu}_{\mu} = F_{\mu\nu,\omega}dx^{\omega} \wedge (d\phi - \theta) - F_{\mu\nu}d\theta$$

$$= F_{\mu\nu,\omega}dx^{\omega} \wedge (d\phi - \theta) - F_{\mu\nu}(F_{\mu'\nu'}dx^{\mu'}dx^{\nu'}) \tag{4.11}$$

$$\Omega^{4}_{\mu} = F_{\mu\nu,\omega}dx^{\omega} \wedge dx^{\nu} - F_{\mu\nu}(d\phi - \theta) \wedge F_{\nu\mu}dx^{\omega} \tag{4.12}$$

Maxwell's equations are essentially

$$F_{\mu\nu,\nu} = J_\mu \tag{4.13}$$

where J_μ is the "current". (It would be zero for a "free field".) Thus,

$$\boxed{\frac{\partial}{\partial x^\nu} \lrcorner\ \Omega^\nu_\mu = J_\mu(d\phi - \theta) - 2F_{\mu\nu}F_{\nu\omega}\ dx^\omega} \tag{4.14}$$

$F_{\mu\nu}F_{\nu\omega}$ --which is *symmetric* in μ and ω --is essentially the *energy-momentum tensor of the electromagnetic field*. Thus, we see that (4.14) provides us with a *geometric* definition of the current and energy-momentum tensor of the electromagnetic field in terms of the Kaluza-Klein notion. This is encouraging!

Similarly,

$$\boxed{\begin{aligned} \frac{\partial}{\partial x^\mu} \lrcorner\ \Omega^4_\mu &= F_{\mu\nu,\mu}dx^\nu + F_{\mu\nu}(d\phi - \theta)F_{\nu\mu} \\ &= -J_\nu dx^\nu - (F_{\mu\nu}F_{\nu\mu})(d\phi - \theta) \end{aligned}} \tag{4.15}$$

We can also readily express these formulas readily in terms of the *Ricci curvature*. (Of course, this is especially interesting for physics, in view of the extra special role this geometric invariant plays in General Relativity.) In general, if Ω^j_i, $1 \leq i,j \leq n$, is the curvature two-form of a Riemannian metric, and if

$$\Omega^j_i = R^j_{ik\ell}dx^k \wedge dx^\ell \quad ,$$

then

$$R_{i\ell} = R^j_{ij\ell}$$

is the *Ricci curvature tensor*. Now,

$$\frac{\partial}{\partial x^j} \lrcorner\ \Omega^j_i = 2R^j_{ij\ell}dx^\ell \tag{4.16}$$

Return to the Kaluza-Klein metric. Let i run from 0 to 4.

$$\frac{\partial}{\partial x^\mu} \lrcorner\ \Omega^\mu_\nu \quad \text{and} \quad \frac{\partial}{\partial x^\mu} \lrcorner\ \Omega^\mu_5$$

are calculated by formulas (4.14) and (4.15).

$$\frac{\partial}{\partial\phi} \lrcorner\, \Omega^4_\mu = \text{, using (4.12)} \qquad (4.17)$$

$$F_{\mu\nu}F_{\mu\omega}dx^\omega$$

Thus,

$$\frac{\partial}{\partial x^\mu} \lrcorner\, \Omega^\mu_\nu + \frac{\partial}{\partial\phi} \lrcorner\, \Omega^4_\nu = J_\nu(d\phi - \theta) - 2F_{\nu\omega}F_{\omega\omega'}dx^{\omega'} + F_{\nu\mu}F_{\mu\omega}dx^\omega$$

$$\boxed{= J_\nu(d\phi - \theta) - 2F_{\nu\mu}F_{\mu\mu'}dx^{\mu'}} \qquad (4.18)$$

We can sum up as follows.

Theorem 4.1. The Maxwell equations (4.13) mean that the fourth component $R_{\nu 4}$ of the Ricci curvature tensor of the Kaluza-Klein metric is equal to J_ν.

This result will generalize to the Yang-Mills equations, giving them a "geometric" interpretation.

5. THE TOTAL GEODESIC PROPERTY OF THE FIBERS OF THE KALUZA-KLEIN METRIC

Y is the space of variables (x^μ,ϕ), X is the space of variables (x^μ). $\pi\colon Y \to X$ is the projection. The fibers of π are the one-dimensional submanifolds

$$x^\mu = \text{constant} \quad .$$

To prove that they are geodesics of the Kaluza-Klein metric, proceed as follows:

$$L' = \frac{1}{2} g_{\mu\nu}\dot{x}^\mu\dot{x}^\nu + (\dot{\phi} - A_\mu\dot{x}^\mu)^2$$

is the Lagrangian for the geodesics. We must show that the curves

$$s \to x^\mu(s) = a^\mu , \qquad \phi = s , \qquad \dot{x}^\nu(s) = 0 , \qquad \dot{\phi} = 1$$

satisfy Lagrange's equations:

$$\frac{\partial L'}{\partial \dot{q}^\mu} = g_{\mu\nu}\dot{x}^\nu - 2(\dot{\phi} - A_\nu\dot{x}^\nu)A_\mu$$

$$= -2A_\mu(a)$$

$$\frac{\partial L}{\partial q^{\mu}} = 0 \quad .$$

$$\frac{\partial L'}{\partial \dot{\phi}} = 2(\dot{\phi}) = 2 , \qquad \frac{d}{ds}\left(\frac{\partial L'}{\partial \dot{\phi}}\right) = 0$$

$$\frac{\partial L'}{\partial \phi} = 0 \quad .$$

Thus we see that Lagrange's equations, for these curves, reduce to an identity. *The fibers are indeed geodesics of the Kaluza-Klein metric.* In turn, as I have shown in [10], this has important global consequences.

6. THE KALUZA-KLEIN SPACE AS A FIBER BUNDLE

Let us examine what this might mean in the general context of Riemannian manifolds and fiber space.

$$\pi : Y \to X$$

is a *submersion map*, i.e., $y \in Y$,

$$\pi_*(Y_y) = X_{\pi(y)} \quad .$$

(Dually, this means that ϕ^* is one-one.) Thus, (Y, X, π) is (by one definition) a *fiber space*.

Kaluza-Klein provides a Riemannian metric for Y. This means that for each $y \in Y_y$ there is a non-degenerate, symmetric bilinear form

$$(v_1, v_2) \to \langle v_1, v_2 \rangle$$

on Y_y. Let $F_y \subset Y_y$ be the tangent space to the fiber, i.e.,

$$F_y = \text{kernel } \pi_* \quad .$$

F_y is a one-dimensional linear subspace of Y_y. It is readily verified that the metric $\langle\,,\rangle$ is non-degenerate when restricted to F_y, hence (by the usual linear algebra)

$$Y_y = F_y \oplus F_y^{\perp} \quad , \tag{6.1}$$

where $F_y^{\perp}$ is the orthogonal complement to F_y with respect to the form $\langle\,,\rangle$, i.e.,

$$F_y^{\perp} = \{v \in Y_y : \langle v, F_y \rangle = 0\} \quad .$$

Now,

$$\pi_* \text{ maps } F_y^{\perp} \textit{ isomorphically } \text{onto } X_{\pi(y)} \quad .$$

The metric $\langle , \rangle$ now (it is readily seen) has the following property:

> π_* is an *isometry* between $\langle , \rangle$ restricted to $F_y^{\perp}$ and $X_{\pi(y)}$, with the metric on $T(X)$ given by *Minkowski*.

We are thus presented with a situation that Bruce Reinhart first treated in the 1950's [4] and called a *bundle-like metric*. I developed the theory further [47] and then it was taken up by Barrett O'Neill [5] who treated the curvature properties in a more definitive way and gave it the more pleasing name *Riemannian submersion*. Later on [2] I dualized the ideas to make them better adapted to the sort of metrics considered in relativity, and called them *homomorphisms between co-Riemannian metrics*. (This would be an appropriate name from a "categorical" point of view.)

Whatever the name, the field $y \to F_y^{\perp}$ of tangent subspaces to Y provides a *connection in the sense of Ehresmann* [28,48] for the fiber space (Y,π,X). This (modulo the usual "completeness" conditions, which we shall assume) defines *parallel transport along curves in* X. If $t \to x(t)$, $a \leq t \leq b$ is such a curve, it defines--by means of "horizontal" lifting, i.e., those curves $t \to y(t)$ such that $\pi y(t) = x(t)$, $dy/dt \in F_{y(t)}^{\perp}$ --a *diffeomorphism* between the fibers $\pi^{-1}(x(a))$ and $\pi^{-1}(x(b))$. As I have shown in [8], the "total geodesic" property of the fibers of π implies that *this parallel transport diffeomorphism* is an isometry between the fibers, where the Riemannian metric is that *induced* on the fibers by the Kaluza-Klein metric. This restricts the *structure group* of the resulting fiber bundles to be a *subgroup* of the group of *isometrics* of the fibers (in this case $SO(2,R)$). In turn, this has physical consequences which will be investigated later on. (For example, it should have something to do with the supposition that, quantum mechanically, "electric charge" is essentially related to the eigenvalues of the infinitesimal generator of *unitary* representations of $SO(2,R)$.) The next task is to compute this parallel transport more explicitly.

7. PARALLEL TRANSPORT FOR THE KALUZA-KLEIN CONNECTION

Return to the more explicit notation. Y has variables (x^{μ},ϕ), X has variables (x^{μ}), $\theta' = A_{\mu}dx^{\mu}$ is the one-form on X which is the *electromagnetic field potential*.

$$ds^2 = g_{\mu\nu} dx^\mu dx^\nu + (d\phi - \theta)^2 \tag{7.1}$$

is the *Kaluza-Klein metric*. The vector fields perpendicular to the fibers of the projection map $\pi: Y \to X$ are those which annihilate

$$d\phi - \theta \equiv d\phi - A_\mu dx^\mu \tag{7.2}$$

This is the *Kaluza-Klein connection*. The vector fields V on Y such that

$$(d\phi - \theta)(V) = 0$$

are the *horizontal vector fields* for the connection. The orbit curves of these vector fields are the *horizontal curves* of the connection. (Keep in mind that it is a connection of Ehresmann type, *not* the "affine connection" for the Kaluza-Klein metric!) We can readily compute the associated parallel transport.

Suppose

$$t \to x(t) = (x^\mu(t))$$

is a curve in X. The "horizontal liftings" of this curve, i.e., the curves in Y which are horizontal and project onto the given curve, determine the parallel transport,

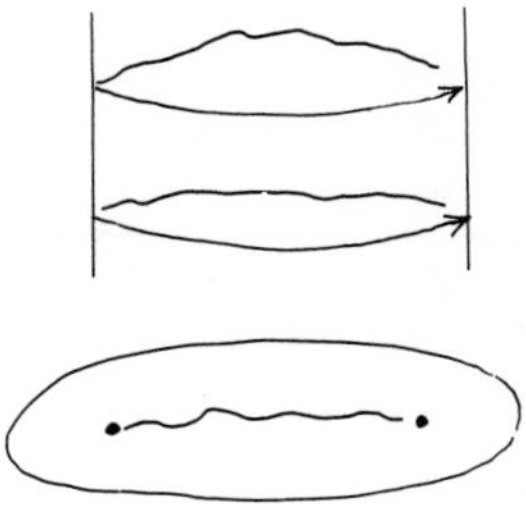

In this case, the equations of the horizontal liftings are especially simple

$$\frac{d\phi}{dt} = A_\mu(x(t)) \frac{dx^\mu}{dt} \quad .$$

Set:

$$\alpha(\phi_0) = (\phi_1)$$

with

$$\phi_1 = \int_0^1 A_\mu(x(t)) \frac{dx^\mu}{dt} \, dt + \phi_0 \quad . \tag{7.3}$$

α is the diffeomorphism of the fibers above the point $x(0)$ to the fiber above the point $x(1)$, resulting from parallel-transporting along the curve.

This is more conveniently interpreted in a group theoretic manner by regarding ϕ as an "angular variable", i.e., the coordinate of the fiber is $e^{i\phi}$. (Now the fiber is identified with $SO(2,R)$.) The parallel-transport diffeomorphism is then

$$e^{i\phi_0} \to e^{i\phi_0} e^{i\int A(x(t))\,dx} \qquad (7.4)$$

i.e., is (with this identification) just *right translation* along the fiber. (The general words are that this is a principal fiber bundle with $SO(2,R)$ as structure group, and that parallel translation is right translation.)

Formula (7.4) will be interesting when we attempt to consider this material quantum-mechanically. It is usual in elementary particle physics to attempt to regard the $A_\mu(x)$ as "operator-valued distributions".

8. PRINCIPAL FIBER BUNDLES AND THEIR ASSOCIATED EHRESMANN CONNECTIONS

Our path is now laid out--generalize the Kaluza-Klein construction to Yang-Mills situations. What we will be dealing with is *principal fiber bundles*

$$\pi: Y \to R^4 \qquad (8.1)$$

whose base space is R^4, and whose "fiber" is a compact Lie group G, *plus* a Riemannian metric on Y such that π is a Riemannian submersion map between it and the Minkowski metric on R^4, such that parallel transport is translation on the Lie group. Before we do this, it is advisable to review some generalities.

Let Y and X be manifolds,

$$\pi: Y \to X$$

a map. Let G be a Lie group which acts as a transformation group on Y.

Definition. The pair consisting of the fiber space (Y,X,π) and the transformation group G is a *principal fiber bundle* with G as *structure group* if the following conditions are satisfied:

a) The orbits of G are precisely the fibers of π, i.e.,

$$\pi(gy) = \pi(y) \quad , \qquad \text{for } g \in G,\ y \in Y,$$

and if $\pi(y) = \pi(y_1)$, then there exists a $g \in G$ such that $y_1 = gy$.

b) G acts *freely*, i.e., if $g \in G$ leaves *one* point of Y fixed, it leaves all points of Y fixed.

c) π is a submersion map, i.e.,

$$\pi_*(Y_y) = X_{\pi(y)} \quad , \qquad \text{for all } y \in Y \ .$$

For most purposes (certainly for ours) it is convenient also to suppose that G acts *effectively*, i.e., that no nonzero element of G acts as the identity on X. With this condition and the ones listed above, *each orbit of* G *on* Y, *i.e., each fiber of* π, *is identified with* G *itself.* However, this identification depends on which point of the fiber one chooses. It turns out that this ambiguity is important.

Now, we consider Ehresmann connections for this principal fiber space, i.e., fields

$$Y \to H_y \subset Y_y$$

of horizontal tangent subspaces with the following property:

> For each curve $t \to x(t)$, $a \le t \le b$, the associated parallel transport diffeomorphism
>
> $$\alpha\colon \pi^{-1}(x(a)) \to \pi^{-1}(x(b))$$
>
> commutes with the action of G.

Such Ehresmann connections will be said to be *compatible* with the principal fiber bundle structure.

The role that such connections play in differential geometry is quite well worked out in the mathematical literature (the book by Kobayashi and Nomizu [48] is the standard reference and I will not delve further into their general theory, at least for the moment).

9. THE SCHRODINGER EQUATION FOR THE KALUZA-KLEIN METRIC. SEMI-CLASSICAL QUANTIZATION

It seems to me (as it has to many others) that one of the prime questions in Yang-Mills land is, particularly in terms of its relation to elementary particle physics,

How to "quantize geometry"?

Now, the Relativists have struggled with this for many years with little to show for it. One of the main messages of this book is the very close relation between gravitation and Yang-Mills; *both involve Riemannian metrics with the "field equations"* defining certain "geometric" relations in the metrics. Thus, one does not seriously expect it to be easy to "quantize Yang-Mills". (This is one of the main reasons that I believe that so much of the current research effort in elementary particle physics is essentially mindless--the "greyhound" physicists jump into any reasonably plausible idea and churn out symbol manipulations and calculations (much of them mumbo-jumbo) without taking any serious look at the meaning. The Gresham-Hermann law then asserts that no one will work on the long-term problems in a serious way precisely because all of these pigs have muddied the water in their habitual fashion. I have seen this happen in many topics for twenty years!)

However, there are interesting *mathematical* things to do with Riemannian metrics, which seem closely related to quantum mechanics, at least of the rather primitive variety. Thus, one can quantize the charged-particle-in-electromagnetic field equations by considering them geodesics of the Kaluza-Klein metric, using the Schrodinger quantum associated with the metric (mathematically, the Laplace-Beltrami operator). One could then attempt "second quantization" as an attempt to make a field theory. (Another possibility is to use the Dirac spinorial analogue of the Laplace-Beltrami operator. I intend to get into this more systematically later on.) I will now look at the first steps for the Kaluza-Klein metric

$$ds^2 = g_{\mu\nu}dx^\mu dx^\nu + (d\phi - A_\mu dx^\mu)^2 \tag{9.1}$$

Let us compute the Laplace-Beltrami operator for this metric. (See my Differential Geometric and the Calculus of Variations; the Second Edition is IM, Volume 18.)

For $f \in \mathscr{F}(Y)$, grad f (read "gradient of f") is the vector field such that

$$V(f) = \langle V, \text{grad } f\rangle$$

$$\text{for} \quad v \in \mathscr{V}(Y)$$

Now, if

$$V = V_i^\mu \frac{\partial}{\partial x^\mu} + V^5 \frac{\partial}{\partial \phi} \quad ,$$

then

$$V(f) = V^\mu \frac{\partial f}{\partial x^\mu} + V^5 \frac{\partial f}{\partial \phi}$$

$$\text{grad } f = f^\mu \frac{\partial}{\partial x^\mu} + f^5 \frac{\partial}{\partial \phi}$$

$$\langle V, \text{grad } f\rangle = g_{\mu\nu} f^\mu V^\nu + (V^5 - A_\mu V^\mu)(f^5 - f^\mu A_\mu)$$

Thus,

$$g_{\mu\nu} f^\nu - A_\mu (f^5 - f^\nu A_\nu) = \frac{\partial f}{\partial x^\mu}$$

$$f^5 - f^\mu A_\mu = \frac{\partial f}{\partial \phi}$$

Thus,

$$f^\mu - A^\mu (f^5 - f^\nu A_\nu) = g^{\mu\nu} \frac{\partial f}{\partial x^\nu}$$

with

$$A^\mu = g^{\mu\nu} A_\nu$$

$$f^\mu = A^\mu \frac{\partial f}{\partial \phi} + g^{\mu\nu} \frac{\partial f}{\partial x^\nu}$$

$$f^5 = \frac{\partial f}{\partial \phi} + A^\mu A_\mu \frac{\partial f}{\partial \phi} + g^{\mu\nu} \frac{\partial f}{\partial x^\nu} A_\mu$$

$$\text{grad } f = \left(A^\mu \frac{\partial f}{\partial \phi} + g^{\mu\nu} \frac{\partial f}{\partial x^\nu}\right) \frac{\partial}{\partial x^\nu} + \left(\frac{\partial f}{\partial \phi} + A^\mu A_\mu \frac{\partial f}{\partial \phi} + g^{\mu\nu} \frac{\partial f}{\partial x^\nu} A_\mu\right) \frac{\partial}{\partial \phi} \tag{9.2}$$

Now ω, the volume element form of the Kaluza-Klein metric, is

$$\omega = dx^0 \wedge \cdots \wedge dx^3 \wedge d\phi \tag{9.3}$$

If $V \in \mathcal{V}(Y)$, $(\text{div } V)$ is the function such that

$$\mathcal{L}_V(\omega) = (\text{div } V)\omega$$

The Laplace-Beltrami operator is now *defined* as

$$f \to \Delta(f) = \text{div}(\text{grad } f) \quad .$$

The Laplace-Beltrami operator can now be *calculated* via (5.2):

$$\Delta(f) = \frac{\partial}{\partial x^\mu}\left(A^\mu \frac{\partial f}{\partial \phi}\right) + \Box(f) + \frac{\partial^2 f}{\partial \phi^2}(1 + A^\mu A_\mu) \tag{9.4}$$

with

$$\Box(f) = g_{\mu\nu} \frac{\partial f}{\partial x^\mu} \frac{\partial f}{\partial x^\nu}$$

the classical D'Alembertian operator.

The eigenvalue problem for Δ,

$$\Delta f = \lambda f \quad ,$$

then would define what one might call "semi-classical quantum mechanics". These equations are not familiar to me and I do not know if they have any interesting structure and/or properties from the physical point of view.

Note one interesting fact:

$$\Delta \frac{\partial}{\partial \phi} = \frac{\partial}{\partial \phi} \Delta \tag{9.5}$$

(Geometrically, this is because the maps

$$(x,\phi) \to (x,\phi+a)$$

form a one-parameter group of isometries of the Kaluza-Klein metric.) The physicist would say that this means that "Δ and $\partial/\partial\phi$ can be simultaneously diagonalized" or that "the observables represented by the Hermitian operators Δ and $i(\partial/\partial\phi)$ can be simultaneously diagonalized". Obviously, the eigenvalues of $i(\partial/\partial\phi)$ should be considered as "electric charge". Thus, we might look for f of the form

$$f = e^{i\lambda\phi} \hat{f}(x)$$

(9.4) then becomes,

$$\Delta(f) = e^{i\lambda\phi}\left(i\lambda \frac{\partial}{\partial x^\mu}(A^\mu \hat{f}) + \Box f - \lambda^2 \hat{f}(1 + A^\mu A_\mu)\right) \tag{9.6}$$

This suggests to me that (qualitatively) there might be an interesting coupling between the charges that appear and the mathematical properties of the linear differential operator in x in the right hand side of (9.6). Presumably, this sort of thing has already been extensively investigated in the study of the "electromagnetic interaction" properties of the Klein-Gordon (and, by extension, the Dirac) equations.

10. THE (LEVI-CIVITA) AFFINE CONNECTION ASSOCIATED WITH A RIEMANNIAN METRIC

As I have emphasized in the study of the classical Kaluza-Klein situation, the Ehresmann connection is not the only object of importance for the physicist; the Riemannian metric on the fiber space provides the all important *field equations*, and perhaps other goodies. (Just as the curvature of a Riemannian metric associated with a gravitational field provides the field equation, i.e., the Einstein equations.) Accordingly, I will now begin the review (roughly following O'Neill [5]) of the calculation of the curvature of a Riemannian metric on the space Y of a submersion map $\pi: Y \to X$ which is a Riemannian submersion. (This topic is quite important elsewhere in physics, e.g., in the calculation of the curvature tensor of a gravitational field-Riemannian metric with certain types of symmetry. This is a typical calculation for relativists who study the properties of "special solutions" of the Einstein gravitational equations.) The first step is to calculate the *affine* connection associated with the metric, which I treat in this section. (Keep in mind the distinction between this affine connection, which is an Ehresmann connection on the *tangent space* to Y, and the Ehresmann connection for the fiber space $Y \to B$ defined by the perpendiculars to the fibers.)

Thus, we can begin with Y as any manifold and with

$$V_1,V_2 \to \langle V_1,V_2\rangle$$

as a non-degenerate, symmetric inner product on vector fields which defines the Riemannian metric. An *affine connection* ∇ for Y is an R-bilinear map

$$(V_1,V_2) \to \nabla_{V_1}V_2 \quad ,$$

mapping $\mathcal{V}(Y) \times \mathcal{V}(Y) \to \mathcal{V}(Y)$, such that

$$\nabla_{fV_1}V_2 = f\nabla_{V_1}V_2$$

$$\nabla_{V_1}(fV_2) = V_1(f)V_2 + f\nabla_{V_1}V_2$$

$$\text{for } V_1,V_2 \in \mathcal{V}(Y) \ ; \qquad f \in \mathcal{F}(Y) \quad .$$

Such an affine metric is said to be *associated* with the Riemannian metric $\langle , \rangle$ if the following conditions are satisfied

$$V_1(\langle V_2,V_3\rangle) = \left\langle \nabla_{V_1}V_2,V_3\right\rangle + \left\langle V_2,\nabla_{V_1}V_3\right\rangle \qquad (10.1)$$

$$\text{for } V_1,V_2,V_3 \in \mathcal{V}(Y) \quad ,$$

$$\nabla_{V_1} V_2 - \nabla_{V_2} V_1 = [V_1, V_2] \tag{10.2}$$

for $V_1, V_2 \in \mathscr{V}(Y)$

(10.1) asserts that the *covariant derivative* of the metric tensor $< , >$ with respect to the affine connection ∇ is *zero*. (9.2) asserts that the affine connection is *torsion free*. (In terms of classical tensor analysis these conditions express the usual symmetry relations among the coefficients of the Christoffel symbols.)

The traditional calculation (presumably due to Levi-Civita, but I have not attempted to trace it) shows that conditions (10.1) and (10.2) *determine* ∇ via an explicit formula. I will now work it through. Set:

$$\delta(V_1, V_2, V_3) = \left\langle \nabla_{V_1}, V_2, V_3 \right\rangle \tag{10.3}$$

Then determining ∇ in terms of $< , >$ is the same thing as determining δ. We shall see that iteration of formulas (10.1) and (10.2), using each in turn, provides the formula for δ.

$$\delta(V_1, V_2, V_3) = V_1(<V_2, V_3>) - \left\langle \nabla_{V_1}, V_3, V_2 \right\rangle$$

$$= V_1(<V_2, V_3>) - \left\langle \nabla_{V_3} V_1, V_2 \right\rangle - <[V_1, V_3], V_2>$$

$$= V_1(<V_2, V_3>) + \left\langle V_1, \nabla_{V_3} V_2 \right\rangle - V_3(<V_1, V_2>) - <[V_1, V_3], V_2>$$

$$= V_1(<V_2, V_3>) + \left\langle V_1, \nabla_{V_2} V_3 + [V_3, V_2] \right\rangle - V_3(<V_1, V_2>)$$

$$- <[V_1, V_3], V_2>$$

$$= V_1(<V_2, V_3>) + <V_1, [V_3, V_2]> - V_3(<V_1, V_2>)$$

$$- <[V_1, V_3], V_2> + V_2(<V_1, V_3>) - \left\langle \nabla_{V_2} V_1, V_3 \right\rangle$$

$$= V_1(<V_2, V_3>) - V_3(<V_1, V_2>) + (<V_1, V_3>) + <V_1, [V_3, V_2]>$$

$$- <V_2, [V_1, V_3]> - \left\langle \nabla_{V_1} V_2, V_3 \right\rangle - <[V_2, V_1], V_3>$$

We have finally come back full circle, and can solve this identity for $\delta(V_1, V_2, V_3)$ for the definitive formula:

$$2\delta(V_1,V_2,V_3) = V_1(\langle V_2,V_3\rangle) - V_3(\langle V_1,V_2\rangle) + V_2(\langle V_1,V_3\rangle) - \langle V_1,[V_2,V_3]\rangle - \langle V_2,[V_1,V_3]\rangle - \langle V_3,[V_2,V_1]\rangle \tag{10.4}$$

We also call this the *Levi-Civita connection*. See [51] for an excellent exposition of this material and of much else that we use.

11. THE LEVI-CIVITA AFFINE CONNECTION INDUCED ON THE FIBER OF A FOLIATION

If $\langle , \rangle$ is a Riemannian metric on a manifold Y and if δ is an R-trilinear map

$$\mathcal{V}(Y) \times \mathcal{V}(Y) \times \mathcal{V}(Y) \to \mathcal{F}(Y)$$

such that

a) $\delta(fV_1,V_2,V_3) = \delta(V_1,V_2,fV_3)$

b) $\delta(V_1,fV_2,V_3) = V_1(f)\langle V_2,V_3\rangle$

c) $\delta(V_1,V_2,V_3) - \delta(V_2,V_1,V_3) = \langle [V_1,V_2],V_3\rangle$

d) $\delta(V_1,V_2,V_3) = V_1(\langle V_2,V_3\rangle) + \delta(V_1,V_3,V_2)$,

it follows from the work of Section 10 that δ is given by formula (10.4) and is equal to

$$\left\langle \nabla_{V_1} V_2, V_3 \right\rangle$$

where ∇ is the Levi-Civita affine connection associated with the metric. In favorable cases this characterization can be used to calculate the affine connection.

For example, suppose that $\mathcal{W} \subset \mathcal{V}(Y)$ is an $\mathcal{F}(Y)$-submodule of $\mathcal{V}(Y)$ such that:

a) $[\mathcal{W},\mathcal{W}] \subset \mathcal{W}$

b) $\dim \mathcal{W}(y) = \text{constant} = m$, as $y \in Y$.

It then follows (Frobenius complete integrability theorem) that $\mathcal{W}$ defines a *foliation* of Y, i.e., an equivalence relation on Y whose equivalence classes are connected submanifolds whose tangent spaces are precisely the tangent subspaces $\mathcal{W}(y) \in Y_y$. These submanifolds are called the *leaves* of the foliation. $\mathcal{W}$ is then identified more geometrically with the set of vector fields on Y which are *tangent to each of the leaves of the foliation.* If the foliation arises from a submersion $\pi\colon Y \to X$ (i.e., if the fibers of π are the leaves of the foliation) then $\mathcal{W}$ consists of the vector fields on Y which are *tangent to the fibers of* π.

Now set:

$$\delta_{\mathcal{W}} = \delta \text{ restricted to } \mathcal{W} .$$

It is clear that $\delta_{\mathcal{W}}$ also satisfies conditions (a) - (d) listed above, hence by uniqueness,

> $\delta_{\mathcal{W}}$ defines the Levi-Civita connection of the leaves of the foliation $\mathcal{W}$.

Set:

$$\mathcal{W}^{\perp} = \{V \in \mathcal{V}(Y)\colon \ <\mathcal{V},\mathcal{W}> = 0\} \tag{11.1}$$

Assume that $\mathcal{V}(Y)$ is a direct sum of $\mathcal{W}$ and $\mathcal{W}^{\perp}$. (This requires that the Riemannian metric--which has not been assumed to be positive definite--is non-degenerate when restricted to the leaves of the foliation.) Define a map

$$\delta^{\perp}_{\mathcal{W}}\colon \mathcal{W} \times \mathcal{W} \otimes \mathcal{W}^{\perp} \to \mathcal{F}(Y)$$

as follows

$$\delta^{\perp}_{\mathcal{W}}(V_1,V_2,V_3) = \delta(V_1,V_2,V_3) \tag{11.2}$$

$$\text{for } V_1,V_2 \in \mathcal{W}, \quad V_3 \in \mathcal{W}^{\perp}$$

$\delta^{\perp}_{\mathcal{W}}$ is essentially *the second fundamental form* of the leaves of the foliation $\mathcal{W}$. Thus,

$$\delta^{\perp}_{\mathcal{W}} = 0 \tag{11.3}$$

is the condition that *all the fibers of* $\delta^{\perp}_{\mathcal{W}}$ *be totally geodesic submanifolds of* Y.

12. THE LEVI-CIVITA AFFINE CONNECTION OF A RIEMANNIAN SUBMERSION MAP

Now suppose Y is a manifold with Riemannian metric $<,>$, $\pi\colon Y \to X$ is a submersion map, and that $\mathcal{W} \subset \mathcal{V}(Y)$ is the $\mathcal{F}(Y)$ submodule of $\mathcal{V}(Y)$

consisting of those vector fields which are tangent to the fibers of π. Let $\mathcal{W}^{\perp}$ denote the orthogonal complement of $\mathcal{W}$ with respect to $<,>$. Suppose that

$$\mathcal{V}(Y) = \mathcal{W} \oplus \mathcal{W}^{\perp} \tag{12.1}$$

The elements of $\mathcal{W}^{\perp}$ are said to be *horizontal vector fields*. An element $V \in \mathcal{V}(X)$ then admits a *unique* horizontal lifting $V_H \in \mathcal{W}^{\perp}$, such that:

$$\pi_*(V_H(y)) = V(\pi(y)) \tag{12.2}$$

for all $y \in Y$

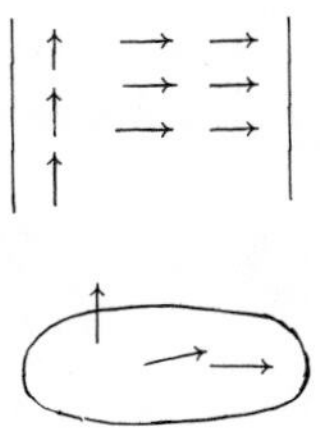

<u>Definition</u>. Suppose X also has a Riemannian metric. The $\pi: Y \to X$ is said to be a *Riemannian submersion map* if

$$<V_H(y), V_H(y)> = <(\pi(y)), V(\pi(y))> \tag{12.3}$$

for all $V \in \mathcal{V}(X)$, $y \in Y$

In words, the metric on X is isomorphic under π_* to the metric on the *horizontal* tangent vectors. We will not make any notational distinction between these two metrics, hoping that the reader can handle any ambiguity.

From now on we shall suppose that Riemannian metrics (not necessarily positive definite) are given on Y and X such that $\pi: Y \to X$ is a Riemannian submersion. We shall suppose that the metric on Y is non-degenerate when restricted to the fibers of π, hence that a vector field on Y can be written in a direct sum way as a sum of vector fields tangent to the fibers of π and perpendicular. This determines an Ehresmann connection for π. This data will be fixed throughout this discussion. The metrics X and Y determine Levi-Civita affine connections, which we will denote as ∇.

Given a vector field V on Y, it can be projected "horizontally" and "vertically", obtaining vector fields that we label

$$\alpha(V), \quad \beta(V) \quad .$$

Thus, α is an $\mathcal{F}(Y)$-linear map: $\mathcal{V}(Y) \to \mathcal{W}^{\perp}$, while β is an $\mathcal{F}(Y)$-linear map: $\mathcal{V}(Y) \to \mathcal{W}$.

$$\alpha + \beta = \text{identity}$$

$$\alpha^2 = \alpha; \qquad \beta^2 = \beta \quad .$$

$$\langle\alpha(\mathcal{V}(Y)), \beta(\mathcal{V}(Y))\rangle = 0 \quad .$$

Here is the first way the Levi-Civita affine connection of the metric on Y is related to that on X.

<u>Theorem 12.1</u>. Given vector fields V_1, V_2 on X, let V_1', V_2' be the "horizontally lifted" vector fields on Y, i.e.,

$$V_1', V_2' \in \mathcal{W}^{\perp}$$

$$\pi_*(V_1') = V_1 \; ; \qquad \pi_*(V_2') = V_2 \quad .$$

Then,

$$\pi_*(\alpha[V_1', V_2']) = [V_1, V_2] \quad . \tag{12.3}$$

<u>Proof</u>. Since V_1', V_2' are π-projectable into X as $[V_1', V_2']$, i.e.,

$$\pi_*([V_1', V_2']) = [V_1, V_2] \quad .$$

Write $[V_1', V_2']$ as the sum of its horizontal and vertical components:

$$[V_1', V_2'] = \alpha[V_1', V_2'] + \beta[V_1', V_2'] \quad .$$

But $\pi_*'\beta = 0$, whence (7.3).

<u>Theorem 12.2</u>. With the notation of Theorem 12.1, we have:

$$\pi_*\left(\alpha\left(\nabla_{V_1'} V_2'\right)\right) = \nabla_{V_1} V_2 \quad . \tag{12.4}$$

Proof. Let V_3 be an additional vector field on X. Let V_3' be its horizontal lifting to a vector field on Y. Then formula (10.4) expresses $\langle\nabla_{V_1}V_2,V_3\rangle$ in terms of the inner product $\langle V_i,V_j\rangle$ and the Jacobi brackets $[V_i,V_j]$, $1 \leq i,j \leq 3$. Similarly, $\langle\nabla_{V_1'}V_2',V_3'\rangle$ can be so expressed. Notice that (with the aid of (12.3)) these two expressions lead to (12.4).

This shows how the Levi-Civita connection on Y is partially determined by that on X. The vertical component of $\nabla_{\mathscr{W}^\perp}\mathscr{W}^\perp$ is also an interesting object, which we discuss next.

13. THE CURVATURE TENSOR OF THE EHRESMANN CONNECTIONS

Continue with $\pi\colon Y \to X$, $\langle\,,\rangle$, $\nabla,\ldots$ as before. Keep in mind that we are dealing with a complicated set of interrelated geometric objects. Note that there are *four* connections floating around: the Levi-Civita *affine* connection of the metric on Y,X and the fibers of π, *plus* the *Ehresmann* connection for the fiber space $\pi\colon Y \to X$. All of them have "curvature" invariants which are also interrelated in complicated ways. In order to continue towards the goal of determining the Levi-Civita connection of the metric on Y (which is the main object of interest from the Kaluza-Klein point of view) in terms of the other objects, we now turn to the "curvature" of the Ehresmann connection. (In the original Kaluza-Klein situation this turned out to be the electromagnetic field. One of the confusing features to keep in mind is that the *curvature* of the Ehresmann connection is directly involved in the Levi-Civita connection.)

Definition. The Ehresmann connection curvature is the bilinear map

$$\gamma\colon \mathscr{W}^\perp \times \mathscr{W}^\perp \to \mathscr{W}$$

defined as follows:

$$\gamma(V_1,V_2) = \beta([V_1,V_2]) \tag{13.1}$$

for $V_1,V_2 \in \mathscr{W}^\perp$.

Theorem 13.1. The Ehresmann connection curvature map is a *tensor field* on Y, i.e., is $\mathscr{F}(Y)$-bilinear.

Proof. For $f \in \mathscr{F}(Y)$,

$$\gamma(V_1,fV_2) = \beta([V_1,fV_2]) = \beta(V_1(f)V_2 + f[V_1,V_2])$$

$$= f\beta([V_1,V_2]) = f\gamma(V_1,V_2) \quad .$$

(Note that $\beta(V_2) = 0$, since V_2 is horizontal, and β is the projection on the vertical fields.)

Here is another way of expressing the Ehresmann curvature tensor. Define a map

$$\Omega\colon \mathcal{V}(X) \times \mathcal{V}(X) \to \mathcal{W}$$

as follows:

$$\Omega(V_1,V_2) = \gamma(V_1',V_2') \tag{13.2}$$

where V_1',V_2' are the horizontal liftings of V_1 and V_2. Note that Ω is a *two-differential form on* X, *with values in the vertical vector fields.* From another point of view, construct the *vector* bundles $E \to X$ whose fiber above the point $x \in X$ is the set of vector fields on the fiber $\pi^{-1}(x)$. Ω is then a "two-differential form on X with values in E". In other words, Ω is a *linear* vector bundle map

$$T(X) \wedge T(X) \to E$$

For a general Ehresmann connection, E has an infinite dimensional fiber. However, for those of "Cartan-Ehresmann type", Ω is the cross-section of a sub-bundle of E with *finite dimensional* fiber consisting of a given Lie algebra (the "structure group" of the connection) of vector fields on the fiber of π.

Notice the geometric meaning of the *vanishing* of the Ehresmann curvature. Then, the horizontal vector fields $\mathcal{W}^{\perp}$ are Frobenius completely integrable.

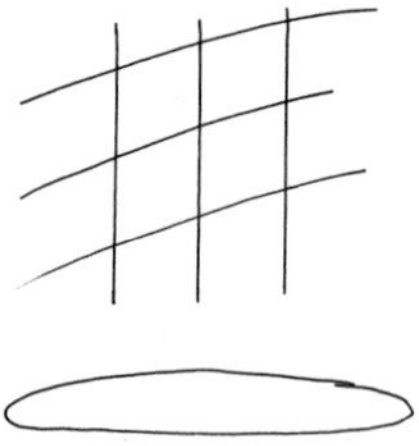

The horizontal curves lie on the leaves of the foliation determined by $\mathcal{W}^{\perp}$. The holonomy group of the connection is *discrete*.

14. THE LEVI-CIVITA AFFINE CONNECTION FOR Y IN TERMS OF THE LEVI-CIVITA CONNECTION FOR X, THE FIBERS OF π, THEIR SECOND FUNDAMENTAL FORMS, AND THE CURVATURE OF THE EHRESMANN CONNECTION

Let V_1, V_2 be vector fields on X with V_1', V_2' their horizontal liftings. We have seen that:

$$\nabla_{V_1'} V_2' = \alpha\left(\nabla_{V_1'} V_2'\right) + \beta\left(\nabla_{V_1'} V_2'\right)$$

$$= \left(\nabla_{V_1} V_2\right)' + \Omega(V_1, V_2) \tag{14.1}$$

This formula shows how the Levi-Civita connection on the horizontal vector fields is determined.

Let $W_1, W_2 \in \mathscr{W}$, i.e., W_1, W_2 are tangent to the fibers of π. Then

$$\nabla_{W_1} W_2 = \alpha\left(\nabla_{W_1} W_2\right) + \beta\left(\nabla_{W_2} W_2\right)$$

$= $ (second fundamental form of fibers of π) (14.2)

$+$ (Levi-Civita connection of the fibers of π applied to W_1, W_2) .

Thus, it only remains to study

$$\nabla_{V_1'} W_1 \quad ,$$

with $V_1' \in \mathscr{W}^\perp$, $W_1 \in \mathscr{W}$. Pick $W_2 \in \mathscr{W}^\perp$, $V_2' \in \mathscr{W}^\perp$.

$$\left\langle \nabla_{V_1'} W_1, W_2 \right\rangle = \left\langle \nabla_{W_1} V_1', W_2 \right\rangle + \langle [V_1', W_1], W_2 \rangle$$

$$= -\left\langle V_1', \nabla_{W_1} W_2 \right\rangle + \langle [V_1', W_1], W_2 \rangle \tag{14.3}$$

$= -$ (second fundamental form of fibers of π) $+ \langle [V_1', W_1], W_2 \rangle$

$$\left\langle \nabla_{V_1'} W_1, V_2' \right\rangle = -\left\langle \nabla_{V_1'} V_2', W_1 \right\rangle$$

$$= -\langle \Omega(V_1, V_2), W_1 \rangle \tag{14.4}$$

$=$ (Ehresmann curvature) .

These formulas make explicit the relation described in the title to this section .

15. THE LEVI-CIVITA CONNECTION FOR THE KALUZA-KLEIN METRIC

As a change of pace from all this generality, I will now return to the basic example:

$$Y = R^5, \qquad X = R^4 .$$

$$ds^2 = g_{\mu\nu} dx^\mu dx^\nu + (d\phi - A_\mu dx^\mu)^2 \tag{15.1}$$

Remember that the usual notation of relativistic physics are used here; μ, ν runs over 0 to 3, with the summation convention. $(g_{\mu\nu})$ is the metric tensor of the Minkowski metric on R^4. The A_μ are functions of x, and represent physically the *potentials of the electromagnetic field*. $\mathscr{V}$, the *vertical* vector fields, is generated by $\partial/\partial\phi$. $\mathscr{V}^\perp$, the horizontal vector fields, is generated by

$$\frac{\partial}{\partial x^\mu} + A_\mu \frac{\partial}{\partial \phi} \equiv h_\mu$$

Thus,

$$\left\langle \frac{\partial}{\partial\phi}, \frac{\partial}{\partial\phi} \right\rangle = 1$$

$$\left\langle \frac{\partial}{\partial\phi}, h_\mu \right\rangle = (d\phi - A_\mu dx^\mu)(h_\mu)$$

$$= A_\mu - A_\mu$$

$$= \underline{\underline{0}}$$

$$\langle h_\mu, h_\nu \rangle = g_{\mu\nu}$$

$$\left[\frac{\partial}{\partial\phi}, h_\mu \right] = 0$$

$$[h_\mu, h_\nu] = \left(\frac{\partial A_\nu}{\partial x^\mu} - \frac{\partial A_\nu}{\partial x^\nu} \right) \frac{\partial}{\partial\phi} \equiv F_{\mu\nu} \frac{\partial}{\partial\phi} \equiv \text{electromagnetic field}$$

We can now use the basic formula (10.4) to compute the Levi-Civita affine connection for the Kaluza-Klein metric (10.1)

$$2\left\langle \nabla_{\frac{\partial}{\partial\phi}} \frac{\partial}{\partial\phi}, \frac{\partial}{\partial\phi} \right\rangle = 0$$

$$2\left\langle \nabla_{\frac{\partial}{\partial\phi}} \frac{\partial}{\partial\phi}, h_\mu \right\rangle = 0$$

Hence,

$$\boxed{\nabla_{\frac{\partial}{\partial\phi}} \frac{\partial}{\partial\phi} = 0} \tag{15.2}$$

(15.2) means that *the fibers of* π *are totally geodesic submanifolds.*

$$2\left\langle \nabla_{h_\mu} \frac{\partial}{\partial\phi}, \frac{\partial}{\partial\phi} \right\rangle = 2\left\langle \nabla_{\frac{\partial}{\partial\phi}} h_\mu, \frac{\partial}{\partial\phi} \right\rangle$$

$$= -2\left\langle h_\mu, \nabla_{\frac{\partial}{\partial\phi}} \frac{\partial}{\partial\phi} \right\rangle$$

$$= \underline{\underline{0}}$$

$$2\left\langle \nabla_{h_\mu} h_\nu, \frac{\partial}{\partial\phi} \right\rangle = -\left\langle \frac{\partial}{\partial\phi}, [h_\nu, h_\mu] \right\rangle$$

$$= \left\langle \frac{\partial}{\partial\phi}, F_{\mu\nu} \frac{\partial}{\partial\phi} \right\rangle$$

$$= F_{\mu\nu}$$

$$\left\langle \nabla_{h_\mu} h_\nu, h_\omega \right\rangle = 0$$

(We know this from general principles, since the metric on X is flat.)

These formulas just reproduce the results we obtained earlier by means of Cartan's method of "moving frame". However, we can now generalize to the Yang-Mills situation.

16. GENERALIZATION OF KALUZA-KLEIN TO YANG-MILLS

Let X continue as R^4 but now let

$$Y = X \times G \quad ,$$

where G is a compact Lie group. Let V, $1 \leq i,j \leq m = \dim G$, be a basis for the left-invariant vector fields on G (i.e., the Lie algebra), with

$$[V_{i,j}] = c_{ij}^k V_k \quad , \tag{16.1}$$

where (c_{ij}^k) are the structure constants of $\mathcal{G}$ (the Lie algebra of G). Since G is *compact*, we can suppose that (c_{ij}^k) is *completely* skew-symmetric.

$\partial/\partial x^\mu$, V^i now form a basis for the vector fields on Y. Set:

$$h_\mu = \frac{\partial}{\partial x^\mu} + A^i_\mu V_i \tag{16.2}$$

The A^i_μ are functions of x, now called the *Yang-Mills field.* Define the metric by the following relations:

$$\begin{aligned} \langle V_i, V_j \rangle &= \delta_{ij} \\ \langle V_i, h_\mu \rangle &= 0 \\ \langle h_\mu, h_\nu \rangle &= g_{\mu\nu} \end{aligned} \tag{16.3}$$

Here are the Jacobi bracket relations computed directly from (16.1) and (16.2):

$$[V_i, h_\mu] = A^j_\mu c^k_{ij} V_k \tag{16.4}$$

$$\begin{aligned} [h_\mu, h_\nu] &= \left[\frac{\partial}{\partial x^\mu} + A^i_\mu V_i, \frac{\partial}{\partial x^\nu} + A^j_\nu V_j\right] \\ &= \partial_\mu (A^j_\nu) V_j - \partial_\nu (A^i_\mu) V_i + A^i_\mu A^j_\nu c^k_{ij} V_k \\ &\equiv F^k_{\mu\nu} V_k \end{aligned} \tag{16.5}$$

with

$$F^k_{\mu\nu} = \frac{\partial A^k_\nu}{\partial x^\mu} - \frac{\partial A^k_\mu}{\partial x^\nu} + A^i_\mu A^j_\nu c^k_{ij} \tag{16.6}$$

(16.6) is the familiar formula in Yang-Mills land. (It is basically the formula $d\theta + \frac{1}{2}[\theta, \theta]$ in terms of Lie algebra-valued one-forms.)

We can now use formula (10.4) to compute the associated Levi-Civita affine connection:

$$\begin{aligned} 2\left\langle \nabla_{V_i} V_j, V_k \right\rangle &= -\langle V_i, [V_j, V_k]\rangle - \langle V_j, [V_i, V_k]\rangle - \langle V_k, [V_j, V_i]\rangle \\ &= -c^i_{jk} - c^j_{ik} - c^k_{ji} \end{aligned}$$

$=$, using the complete skew-symmetry of the structure constants, i.e., the compactness of G,

$$c^k_{ij} \tag{16.7}$$

$$2\left\langle \nabla_{V_i} V_j, h_\mu \right\rangle = - \langle V_i, [V_j, h_\mu] \rangle - \langle V_j, [V_i, h_\mu] \rangle - \langle h_\mu, [V_j, V_i] \rangle$$

$$= -A^k c^i_{jk} - A^k c^j_{ik} - 0$$

$$= 0 \quad , \tag{16.8}$$

again because of the compactness of G. Thus, (16.7) and (16.8) express the relation

$$\boxed{\nabla_{V_i} V_j = \frac{1}{2} c^k_{ij} V_k} \tag{16.9}$$

which in turn says that

The fibers of π are totally geodesic. The affine connection induced on them is just that of a compact Lie group with the bi-invariant Riemannian metric.	(16.10)

Now, using (10.4) again:

$$\frac{1}{2} \left\langle \nabla_{h_\mu} h_\nu, V_i \right\rangle = -\langle h_\mu, [h_\nu, V_i] \rangle - \langle h_\nu, [h_\mu, V_i] \rangle - \langle V_i, [h_\nu, h_\mu] \rangle$$

$$= \text{, using (16.4) and (16.5),}$$

$$\boxed{F^i_{\mu\nu}} \tag{16.11}$$

Again, we know that

$$\boxed{\left\langle \nabla_{h_\mu} h_\mu, h_\omega \right\rangle = 0} \quad ,$$

since the metric on X is flat, and the projection $\pi: Y \to X$ is a Riemannian submersion.

These formulas provide the Levi-Civita connection. Notice that the A^i_μ *only influence them through its curvature* (16.11). The role of the "potentials" has been pushed into the "geometry", i.e., into the definition of the metric. We will call this metric on $Y = X \times G$ the *Kaluza-Klein-Yang-Mills metric.*

17. THE GEODESICS OF THE KALUZA-KLEIN-YANG-MILLS METRIC

With the formulas of Section 16, we can readily compute the geodesics of the metric. Projected down to X, they would be the generalizations to Yang-Mills of the classical equations for a charged particle in an electromagentic field. (These equations have also been studied by Shlomo Sternberg [49]. In fact, his work partially suggested mine.)

Let

$$t \to y(t)$$

be a curve in $Y = X \times G$ which is a geodesic. Let $t \to \dot{y}(t)$ denote its tangent vector. Suppose that

$$\dot{y}(t) = z^i(t)V_i + z\ (t)h_\mu \quad . \tag{17.1}$$

$$\begin{aligned} \nabla_{\dot{y}(t)}\dot{y}(t) &= \frac{dz^i}{dt}V_i + \frac{dz^\mu}{dt}h_\mu + z^i\nabla_{\dot{y}(t)}V_i + z^\mu\nabla_{\dot{y}(t)}h_\mu \\ &= \frac{dz^i}{dt}V_i + \frac{dz^\mu}{dt}h_\mu + z^iz^j\nabla_{V_j}V_i + z^iz^\mu\nabla_{h_\mu}V_i + z^\mu z^j\nabla_{V_j}h_\mu \\ &\qquad + z^\mu z^\nu\nabla_{h_\mu}h_\nu \end{aligned} \tag{17.2}$$

As a consequence of the formulas of Section 16, note that:

$$z^iz^j\nabla_{V_j}V_i = 0 \tag{17.3}$$

(Again, this is a consequence of the compactness of G.)

$$0 = \left\langle \nabla_{V_j}h_\mu, V_i \right\rangle$$

$$\begin{aligned} \left\langle \nabla_{V_j}h_\mu, h_\nu \right\rangle &= \left\langle \nabla_{h_\mu}V_j, h_\mu \right\rangle + <[V_j,h_\mu],h_\nu> \\ &= -\left\langle V_j, \nabla_{h_\mu}h\nu \right\rangle \\ &= -2F^j_{\mu\nu} \end{aligned}$$

$$\begin{aligned} \left\langle \nabla_{h_\mu}V_i, V_j \right\rangle &= \left\langle \nabla_{V_j}h_\mu, V_j \right\rangle + <[h_\mu,V_i],V_j> \\ &= -A^jc^k_{ij}<V_k,V_j> \\ &= 0 \end{aligned}$$

$$\left\langle \nabla_{h_\mu} V_i, h_\nu \right\rangle = - \left\langle V_i, \nabla_{h_\mu} h_\nu \right\rangle - 2F^i_{\mu\nu}$$

We can now express the condition that $t \to y(t)$ is a geodesic, i.e., that

$$\nabla_{\dot{y}(t)} \dot{y}(t) = 0$$

$$0 = \left\langle V_j, \nabla_{\dot{y}(t)} \dot{y}(t) \right\rangle$$

$$= \frac{dz^j}{dt} + z^i z^\mu \left\langle V_j, \nabla_{h_\mu} V_i \right\rangle + z^\mu z^i \left\langle V_j, \nabla_{V_i} h_\mu \right\rangle$$

$$- z^\mu z^\nu \left\langle V_j, \nabla_{h_\mu} h_\mu \right\rangle$$

i.e.,

$$0 = \frac{dz^j}{dt} - 2z^\mu z^\nu F^j_{\mu\nu} \tag{17.4}$$

$$0 = \left\langle h_\mu, \nabla_{\dot{y}(t)} \dot{y}(t) \right\rangle$$

$$= g_{\mu\nu} \frac{dz^\mu}{dt} + z^i z^\mu \left\langle h_\nu, \nabla_{h_\mu} V_i \right\rangle + z^\mu z^j \left\langle h_\nu, \nabla_{V_j} h_\mu \right\rangle$$

$$= g_{\mu\nu} \frac{dz^\mu}{dt} - 2z^i z^\mu \quad V_i, \nabla_{h_\mu} h_\mu$$

or

$$g_{\mu\nu} \frac{dz^\mu}{dt} + 4F^i_{\mu\nu} z^i z^\mu = 0 \tag{17.5}$$

Notice the remarkable "decoupled" nature of Equations (17.4) and (17.5). Of course, the z^i, z^μ are the strange beasts called *quasi-coordinates* in analytical mechanics. The $F^i_{\mu\nu}$ are functions of x, so that we must ultimately reduce (17.4) and (17.5) to more complicated equations for $x(t)$, dx/dt, d^2x/dt. One can do this using Equation (17.1):

$$\dot{y}(t) = z^i(t)V_i + z^\mu(t)\left(\frac{\partial}{\partial x^\mu} - A^i_\mu V_i\right)$$

$$= (z^i(t) - z^\mu(t)A^i_\mu(x(t)))V_i + z^\mu(t)\frac{\partial}{\partial x^\mu} \qquad (17.6)$$

Hence,

$$z^\mu(t) = \frac{dx^\mu}{dt} \qquad (17.7)$$

The *quantization* of these geodesic equations should be important for the study of the quantum mechanics of Yang-Mills fields. I plan to get to this later on. As preparation for this I will now indicate how these geodesic equations can be described in the more traditional ways in terms of Lagrange's equations.

18. THE KALUZA-KLEIN-YANG-MILLS GEODESICS IN TERMS OF LAGRANGE'S EQUATIONS

Continue with

$$Y = R^4 \times G \quad .$$

V_i (the left-invariant vector fields on G) and the vector field

$$h_\mu = \frac{\partial}{\partial x^\mu} + A^i_\mu V_i$$

form a base for vector fields on Y. The metric generates the following relations:

$$\langle V_i, V_j\rangle = \delta_{ij}$$

$$\langle V_i, h_\mu\rangle = 0$$

$$\langle h_\mu, h_\nu\rangle = g_{\mu\nu} \quad .$$

Let (ω^i, ω^μ) be the dual basis for one-forms, i.e.,

$$\omega^i(V_j) = \delta^i_j \; ; \qquad \omega^i(h_\mu) = 0$$

$$\omega^\mu(h_\nu) = \delta^\mu_\nu \; ; \qquad \omega^\mu(V_j) = 0$$

Thus, the metric is given as

$$ds^2 = \omega^i \cdot \omega^i + g_{\mu\nu}\omega^\mu \cdot \omega^\nu$$

($\cdot$ means symmetric product of one-forms.) Let θ^i be the left-invariant one-form on G dual to the V_i, i.e.,

$$\theta^i(V_j) = \delta^i_j \quad .$$

(The θ^i are called the *Cartan-Maurer forms* in Lie theory.) Then,

$$\omega^i = \theta^i - A^i_\mu dx^\mu$$

$$\omega^\mu = dx^\mu$$

Thus, the Kaluza-Klein-Yang-Mills metric is

$$ds^2 = (\theta^i - A^i_\mu dx^\mu)(\theta^i - A^i_\mu dx^\mu) + g_{\mu\nu}dx^\mu dx^\nu \tag{18.1}$$

This formula also makes it evident how this metric is a generalization of the Kaluza-Klein metric associated with the electromagnetic field.

Suppose that (ϕ^i) is a coordinate system for G with

$$\theta^i = a^i_j(\phi)dx^j$$

Let $L\colon T(Y) \to R$ be the function defined as follows

$$L = (a^i_j\dot{\phi}^j - A^i_\mu\dot{x}^\mu)(a^i_k\dot{\phi}^k - A^i_\mu\dot{x}^\mu) + g_{\mu\nu}\dot{x}^\mu\dot{x}^\nu \tag{18.2}$$

We can write down the equations of the geodesics in the usual Lagrange way:

$$\begin{aligned} \frac{d}{dt}\frac{\partial L}{\partial\dot{\phi}^i} - \frac{\partial L}{\partial\phi^i} &= 0 \\ \frac{d}{dt}\frac{\partial L}{\partial\dot{x}^\mu} - \frac{\partial L}{\partial x^\mu} &= 0 \end{aligned} \tag{18.3}$$

$$\frac{\partial L}{\partial\dot{\phi}^i} = 2a^j_i(a^j_k\dot{\phi}^k - A^j_\mu\dot{x}^\mu)$$

$$\frac{\partial L}{\partial\phi^i} = 2\left(\frac{\partial a^\ell_j}{\partial\phi^i}\dot{\phi}^j\right)(a^\ell_k\dot{\phi}^k - A^\ell_\mu\dot{x}^\mu)$$

$$\frac{\partial L}{\partial\dot{x}^\mu} = -2A^i_\mu(a^i_k\dot{\phi}^k - A^i_\nu\dot{x}^\nu)g_{\mu\nu}\dot{x}^\nu$$

$$\frac{\partial L}{\partial \dot{x}^\mu} = -2 \frac{\partial A_\nu^i \dot{x}^\nu}{\partial x^\mu} (a_k^i \dot{\phi}^k - A_\omega^i \dot{x}^\omega)$$

The specific equations are complicated. (However, perhaps it would be worthwhile to study them numerically.) Note that they take the following general form:

$$\frac{d^2x}{dt^2} = f\left(x, \frac{dx}{dt}, \phi, \frac{d\phi}{dt}\right) \tag{18.4}$$

$$\frac{d^2\phi}{dt^2} = g\left(x, \frac{dx}{dt}, \phi, \frac{d\phi}{dt}\right) \tag{18.5}$$

This is somewhat reminiscent of an "input system" as considered in Mathematical Systems Theory with ϕ the "input", $(x, dx/dt)$ the state, and with (18.5) some sort of "feedback". Note also the relations with the general idea of a *"classical mechanics spinning particle"*, as described in "Interdisciplinary Mathematics", Volume 10.

19. CURVATURE OF A RIEMANNIAN SUBMERSION

As I have already pointed out, from the mathematical point of view (and presumably also the "physical"), the chief motivation for introducing a Riemannian metric into the study of Yang-Mills fields is that we have all the resources of Riemannian geometry available, and this is the most highly developed and sophisticated area of geometry. The role that the *curvature tensor* plays is particularly important. In this section I will develop some formulas that are useful for calculating curvature.

Let Y be a manifold with a Riemannian metric $\langle , \rangle$. Let ∇ be the associated Levi-Civita affine connection. (The explicit expression for ∇ in terms of $\langle , \rangle$ and Jacobi bracket is given by formula (10.4).) The *curvature tensor* is an $\mathcal{F}(Y)$-trilinear map

$$R: \mathcal{V}(Y) \times \mathcal{V}(Y) \times \mathcal{V}(Y) \to \mathcal{V}(Y)$$

defined as follows:

$$R(V_1,V_2)(V_3) = \nabla_{V_1}(\nabla_{V_2}V_3) - \nabla_{V_2}(\nabla_{V_1}V_3) - \nabla_{[V_1,V_2]}(V_3) \tag{19.1}$$

for $V_1,V_2,V_3 \in \mathcal{V}(Y)$.

Set:

$$K(V_1,V_2,V_3,V_4) = \langle V_4,R(V_1,V_2)(V_3)\rangle \tag{19.2}$$

Then,

$$K(V_1,V_2,V_3,V_4) = \left\langle V_4,\nabla_{V_1}\nabla_{V_2}V_3\right\rangle - \left\langle V_4,\nabla_{V_2}\nabla_{V_1}V_3\right\rangle - \left\langle V_4,\nabla_{[V_1,V_2]}V_3\right\rangle$$

$$= V_1\left(\left\langle V_4,\nabla_{V_2}V_3\right\rangle\right) - \left\langle \nabla_{V_1}V_4, \nabla_{V_2}V_3\right\rangle - V_2\left(\left\langle V_4,\nabla_{V_1}V_3\right\rangle\right) + \left\langle \nabla_{V_2}V_4,\nabla_{V_1}V_3\right\rangle - \left\langle V_4,\nabla_{[V_1,V_2]}V_3\right\rangle \quad (19.2)$$

Formula (19.2) expresses the curvature tensor in terms of *single* covariant derivatives and Lie derivatives. This formula is a useful starting point for the study of curvature of Riemannian submersions (following O'Neill [5]).

Now, suppose X is a manifold with a Riemannian metric and that $\pi: Y \to X$ is a Riemannian submersion map. Let $\mathcal{W} \subset \mathcal{V}(Y)$ be the vector fields tangent to the fibers of π, and let $\mathcal{W}^{\perp}$ be their orthogonal complement. Then, $\mathcal{W}$ are the *vertical vectors*, $\mathcal{W}^{\perp}$ the *horizontal*, for the Ehresmann connection.

Let K_X be the curvature object defined via formula (19.2) for X. For $V_1,V_2,V_3,V_4 \in \mathcal{V}(X)$, let $V_1',V_2',V_3',V_4' \in \mathcal{W}^{\perp}$ be their horizontal lifting to vector fields on Y.

Theorem 19.1.

$$\pi^*(K_X(V_1,V_2,V_3,V_4)) = K(V_1',V_2',V_3',V_4') \quad . \quad (19.3)$$

Proof. This follows from (19.2), the formula

$$\pi^*\left(\left\langle V_1,\nabla_{V_2}V_3\right\rangle\right) = \left\langle V_1',\nabla_{V_2'}V_3'\right\rangle \quad (19.4)$$

that we have already proved, and the formula

$$\pi^*(\langle V_1,V_2\rangle) = \langle V_1',V_2'\rangle \quad (19.5)$$

that *characterizes* a Riemannian submersion.

20. CURVATURE OF THE KALUZA-KLEIN-YANG-MILLS METRIC

Let us return to the situation of Section 16. $Y = X \times G$, X = Minkowski space, G = compact Lie group. $\mathcal{W}$ has a basis composed of vector fields

$$V_i \quad , \qquad 1 \leq i,j \leq n = \dim G \quad ,$$

with

$$\langle V_i, V_j \rangle = \delta_{ij}$$

$$[V_i, V_j] = c_{ij}^k V_k$$

$\mathcal{W}^\perp$ has a basis consisting of

$$h_\mu \quad , \qquad 0 \leq \mu, \quad \nu \leq 3 \quad .$$

$$\langle V_1, h_\mu \rangle = 0$$

$$\langle h_\mu, h_\nu \rangle = g_{\mu\nu}$$

In Section 16 we derived the following covariant derivative and Jacobi bracket relations:

$$[V_i, h_\mu] = A_\mu^j c_{ij}^k V_k$$

$$[h_\mu, h_\nu] = F_{\mu\nu}^k V_k$$

$$\nabla_{V_i} V_j = \frac{1}{2} [V_i, V_j]$$

$$\frac{1}{2} \left\langle \nabla_{h_\mu} h_\nu, V_i \right\rangle = F_{\mu\nu}^i$$

$$\left\langle \nabla_{h_\mu} h_\nu, h_\omega \right\rangle = 0$$

Theorem 19.1 now implies that

$$K(h_\mu, h_\nu, h_{\mu'}, h_{\nu'}) = 0 \tag{20.1}$$

$$R(V_i, V_j)(V_k) = \nabla_{V_i}\left(\nabla_{V_j}(V_k)\right) - \nabla_{V_j}\left(\nabla_{V_i}(V_k)\right) - \nabla_{[V_i,V_j]} V_k$$

$$= \frac{1}{4} [V_i, [V_j, V_k]] - \frac{1}{4} [V_j, [V_i, V_k]] - \frac{1}{2} [[V_i, V_j], V_k]$$

$$= \frac{1}{4}[V_i,[V_j,V_k]] + \frac{1}{4}[[V_i,V_k],V_j] - \frac{1}{2}[[V_i,V_j],V_k]$$

$$= -\frac{1}{2}[[V_i,V_j],V_k] \qquad (20.2)$$

Thus the curvature of the fibers of π is essentially just that of a compact Lie group with a bi-invariant metric. This is a symmetric space in the sense of Elie Cartan and almost everything conceivable is known about the Riemannian geometry (curvature, geodesics, etc.) of these spaces.

Now,

$$\nabla_{h_\mu} h_\nu = 2F^i_{\mu\nu} V_i$$

Hence,

$$\nabla_{h_{\mu'}} \nabla_{h_\mu} h_\nu = 2h_{\mu'}(F^i_{\mu\nu})V_i - 2F^i_{\mu\nu}\nabla_{h_{\mu'}} V_i \qquad (20.3)$$

$$\left\langle \nabla_{h_\mu} V_i, h_\nu \right\rangle = -\left\langle V_i, \nabla_{h_\mu} h_\nu \right\rangle$$

$$= -2F^i_{\mu\nu}$$

$$\left\langle \nabla_{h_\mu} V_i, V_j \right\rangle = \left\langle \nabla_{V_i} h_\mu, V_j \right\rangle + \langle [h\ , V_i] V_j \rangle$$

$$= 0 - A^j_\mu c^k_{ij} \delta_{ik}$$

$$= 0$$

(since c^k_{ij} is *completely* skew-symmetric). Hence,

$$\nabla_{h_\mu} V_i = -2F^i_{\mu\nu} g^{\nu\nu'} h_{\nu'} \qquad (20.4)$$

Insert (20.4) into (20.3):

$$\nabla_{h_{\mu'}} \nabla_{h_\mu} h_\nu = 2h_{\mu'}(F^i_{\mu\nu})V_i + 4F^i_{\mu\nu} F^i_{\mu'\omega} g^{\omega\omega'} h_{\omega'} \qquad (20.5)$$

Hence,

$$R(h_{\mu'},h_\mu)(h_\nu) = 2h_{\mu'}(F^i_{\mu\nu})V_i - 2h_\mu(F^i_{\mu'\nu})V_i + 4F^i_{\nu\mu}F^i_{\mu'\omega} - g^{\omega\omega'}h_{\omega'}$$

$$- 4F_{\mu'\nu}F_{\mu\omega}g^{\omega\omega'}h_{\omega'} - \nabla_{[h_{\mu'},h_\mu]}h_\nu$$

(20.6)

$$\nabla_{[h_{\mu'},h_\mu]} h_\nu = \nabla_{F^k_{\mu'\mu}V_k} h_\nu$$

$$= F^k_{\mu'\mu}\nabla_{V_k} h_\nu$$

$$= F^k_{\mu'\mu}\nabla_{h_\nu} V_k - F^k_{\mu'\mu}[V_k,h_\nu]$$

$$= -2F^k_{\mu'\mu}F^k_{\nu\omega}g^{\omega\omega'}h_{\omega'} - F^k_{\mu'\mu}A^j_\mu c^i_{kj}V_i \tag{20.7}$$

Putting together (20.6) and (20.7) gives

$$R(h_{\mu'},h_\mu)(h_\nu) = (2\partial_{\mu'}(F'_{\mu\nu}) - 2\partial_\mu(F_{\mu'\nu}) - F^k_{\mu'\mu}A^j_\nu c^i_{kj})V_i \tag{20.8}$$

$$+ 4(F^i_{\mu\nu}F^i_{\mu'\omega}g^{\omega\omega'}h_{\omega'} - F^i_{\mu'\nu}F^i_{\mu\omega}g^{\omega\omega'} + \tfrac{1}{2}F^i_{\mu'\mu}F^i_{\nu\omega}g^{\omega\omega'})h_{\omega'}$$

The other parts of the curvature tensor can be computed similarly. The first three terms on the right hand side of (20.8) can be further simplified using the Bianchi identity, but I will not go into that here.

21. RIEMANNIAN SUBMERSIONS WITH TOTALLY GEODESIC FIBERS. STEENROD FIBER BUNDLES WITH STRUCTURE GROUPS

Let us return to the general situation, motivated by the observation already made that the *Yang-Mills-Kaluza-Klein metric admits a Riemannian submersion whose fibers are all totally geodesic submanifolds*. This suggests that it is worthwhile to study such objects in general [8]. Suppose then that

$$\pi: Y \to X$$

is a map between Riemannian manifolds which defines a *Riemannian submersion* between them. We suppose the metric on Y is non-degenerate when restricted to the fibers of π. This defines an *Ehresmann connection* for the fiber space (π,Y,X); the *horizontal vectors* are those which are perpendicular to the fibers of π. We suppose this connection is *complete*, i.e., each curve $t \to \sigma(t)$, $a \leq t \leq b$ in X can be lifted to a *horizontal* curve in Y beginning at our arbitrary point in the fiber $\pi^{-1}(\sigma(a))$. (This is not the standard terminology.) Thus, there is a diffeomorphism

$$\phi_\sigma: \pi^{-1}(\sigma(a)) \to \pi^{-1}(\sigma(b)) \quad ,$$

called *parallel transport*, obtained by following, for each $y \in \pi^{-1}(\sigma(a))$, the horizontal curve which covers σ and which begins at y for $t = a$. In particular, the ϕ_σ, for σ a *loop*, i.e., $\sigma(a) = \sigma(b)$, defines a *group* of diffeomorphisms of the fiber $\pi^{-1}(\sigma(a))$.

Theorem 21.1. If all the fibers of π are totally geodesic submanifolds of the Riemannian manifold Y, then each parallel transport diffeomorphism is an *isometry* of the Riemannian metric induced on the fibers.

Proof. Let V be a horizontal vector field on Y which is projectable under π, i.e., there is a vector field V' on X such that

$$\pi_*(V(y)) = V'(\pi(y)) \qquad (21.1)$$

for all $y \in Y$.

Let $t \to \phi_t$ be the one-parameter group of diffeomorphisms of Y generated by V, i.e., the orbit curves of the group

$$t \to \phi_t(y)$$

are the orbit curves of the vector field V. Condition (21.1) means that:

ϕ_t preserves the fibers of π,
i.e., maps fibers into fibers.

It is readily seen that the parallel transport along a curve $t \to \sigma(t)$, $0 \le t \le b$, which is an orbit curve of V', is *equal* to ϕ_b. It suffices to prove Theorem 21.1 for curves of this type, since an arbitrary curve can be built up by putting curves of this type together piece-by-piece.

Let V_1, V_2 be vector fields on Y which are vertical, i.e., which are tangent to the fibers of π. Then

$$\begin{aligned} V(\langle V_1,V_2\rangle) &= \langle \nabla_V V_1, V_2\rangle + \langle V_1, \nabla_V V_2\rangle \\ &= \langle \nabla_{V_1} V, V_2\rangle + \langle [V,V_1],V_2\rangle + \langle \nabla_{V_2} V, V_1\rangle + \langle [V,V_2],V_1\rangle \\ &= -\langle V, \nabla_{V_1} V_2\rangle + \langle [V,V_1],V_2\rangle - \langle V, \nabla_{V_2} V_1\rangle + \langle [V,V_2],V_1\rangle \end{aligned}$$

Now, if all fibers of π are totally geodesic submanifolds, $\nabla_{V_1} V_2$ is also vertical, hence

$$\begin{aligned} 0 &= \langle V, \nabla_{V_1} V_2\rangle \\ &= \langle V, \nabla_{V_2} V_1\rangle \end{aligned}$$

Hence,

$$V(\langle V_1,V_2\rangle) = \langle [V,V_1],V_2\rangle + \langle [V,V_2],V_1\rangle$$

for V_1,V_2 *vertical.*

Thus, if

$$0 = [V,V_1] = -[V,V_2] \tag{21.2}$$

then

$$V(\langle V_1,V_2\rangle) = 0 \quad . \tag{21.3}$$

In particular,

$$\phi_t^*(\langle V_1,V_2\rangle) = 0 \quad . \tag{21 4}$$

(21.2) means that

$$\phi_{t_*}(V_1) = V_1 \ ; \qquad \phi_{t_*}(V_2) = V_2$$

hence,

$$\begin{aligned}\langle \phi_{t*}((V_1(y)), \phi_{t*}(V_2(y))\rangle &= \langle V_1(\phi_t y), V_2(\phi_t y)\rangle \\ &= \phi_t^*(\langle V_1,V_2\rangle)(y) \\ &= \text{, using (21.4)} \\ &\quad \langle V_1,V_2\rangle(y) \\ &= \langle V_1(y),V_2(y)\rangle\end{aligned}$$

Given any two vertical vectors $v_1,v_2 \in Y_y$, one can *locally* find vertical vector fields V_1,V_2 satisfying (21.2) and $V_1(y) = v_1$, $V_2(y) = v_2$. Thus, ϕ_t is, for t sufficiently small, an isometry between fibers. The process can then be contined in t, to prove for $t = b$.

<u>Exercise</u>. Fill in the details of the proof, i.e., that such vector fields V_1,V_2 can be found *locally*. (This involves using the Implicit Function Theorem and the hypothesis that π is a submersion.)

Suppose one is given such a Riemannian submersion map $\pi\colon Y \to X$ whose fibers are totally geodesic submanifolds. For the applications to Yang-Mills theory, it is extremely important to discuss the global, topological properties of such "fiber spaces". To do so, one would like to use the standard machinery developed by topologists to study fiber spaces and fiber bundles. The standard reference is the book by Steenrod [52]. Later on, we shall apply this machinery in detail. In this section I want--as a preliminary step--to present a reasonable condition which *assures* that (π, Y, X) is indeed a "fiber bundle" in the Steenrod sense, with a "structure group" G which is a *Lie group* and which can be *computed in terms of the natural differential geometric invariants.*

Theorem 21.2. Let $\pi: Y \to X$ be a Riemannian submersion map, all of whose fibers are totally geodesic and non-degenerate Riemannian submanifolds. Further, suppose that X is a connected space and that π is a proper map, i.e., the inverse image of each compact subset of X is a compact subset of Y. Let G be the holonomy group of the Ehresmann connection determined by the metric. Then G is a Lie group and (π, Y, X) is a fiber bundle, with structure group G, in the sense of Steenrod.

I will not go into the details of the proof here [8]. It is basically very straightforward. Pick a point $x_0 \in X$ and a sufficiently small open subset U of X containing x_0. Then, using the submersion hypothesis about π (and the Implicit Function Theorem) and the properness, we see that U can be chosen so that

$$\pi^{-1}(U) \text{ is diffeomorphic to a product}$$
$$U \times F, \text{ with } F = \pi^{-1}(x_0).$$

Further, this diffeomorphism can be realized by assigning to a point $y \in \phi^{-1}(U)$ the point $(x,f) \in U \times F$, where

$$x = \pi(y)$$

$$f = \text{end-point of geodesic starting at } y, \text{ ending } \textit{perpendicularly} \text{ on } F.$$

($\pi^{-1}(U)$ is a *geodesic tubular neighborhood* of F.)

Now, this local product decomposition can be "parallel transported" around to other points of X along curves. Two different decompositions obtained in this way will differ by an element of the holonomy group, i.e., G. That G is a Lie group is a consequence of Theorem 21.1 and Yamabe's theorem of Lie group theory [48]-- G is an *arcwise-connected subgroup of a Lie group*--namely the group of isometries of the metric on the fiber F, hence itself a Lie group.

This result--even though it is essentially "trivial" (after one knows a certain amount of machinery) is the cornerstone of the approach to Gauge Fields that I am developing here. The point is that a type of differential geometric structure guarantees (in principle) the *classification* of the *global* possibilities. If there is any relatively simple "rationality" in the structure of elementary particles, it is, in my opinion, only likely to come from some such global structure.

BIBLIOGRAPHY

1. E. Cartan, Oeuvres Complètes, Partie III, Gauthier-Villars, Paris, 1952.

2. C. Ehresmann, Les connexions infinitésimales dans un espace fibré, Colloque de Topologie, Bruxelles, 1950.

3. J. Dieudonné, Treatise on Analysis, Volume 4, Academic Press, New York, 1974.

4. B. Reinhart, Foliated manifolds with bundle-like metrics, Ann. of Math. 69 (1959), 119-132.

5. B. O'Neill, Submersions and geodesics, Duke Math. J. 34 (1967), 363-373.

6. R. Hermann, Sur les isométries infinitésimaux et le groupe d'holonomie d'un éspace de Riemann, C.R. Acad. Sci Paris 239 (1954), 1178-1180.

7. R. Hermann, Sur les automorphismes infinitésimaux d'une G'structure, C.R. Acad. Sci. Paris 239 (1954), 1760-1761.

8. R. Hermann, A sufficient condition that a map of Riemannian manifolds be a fiber bundle, Proc. Am. Math. Soc. 11 (1960), 236.

9. R. Hermann, Existence in the large of totally geodesic submanifolds of Riemannian spaces, Bull. Am. Math. Soc. 66 (1960), 59-61.

10. R. Hermann, The differential geometry of foliations, II, J. Math. Mech. 11 (1962), 303-316.

11. R. Hermann, Existence in the large of parallelism homomorphisms, Trans. Am. Math. Soc. 161 (1963), 170-183.

12. R. Hermann, Cartan connections and the equivalence problems for geometric structures, Contributions to Differential Equations 3 (1964), 199-248.

13. R. Hermann, Analytic continuation of group representations, Comm. Math. Phys. 2 (1966), 251-270.

14. R. Hermann, Analytic continuation of group representations, II, Comm. Math. Phys. 3 (1966), 53-74.

15. R. Hermann, Analytic continuation of group representations, III, Comm. Math. Phys. 3 (1966), 75-97.

16. R. Hermann, Equivalence of submanifolds of homogeneous spaces, Math. Ann. 158 (1965), 284-289.

17. R. Hermann, Lie Groups for Physicists, W.A. Benjamin, New York, 1966.

18. R. Hermann, Differential Geometry and the Calculus of Variations, Academic Press, New York, 1969 (2nd edition, Math Sci Press, 1977).

19. R. Hermann, Analytic Continuation of Group Representations, Part IV, Comm. Math. Phys. 5 (1967), 131-156; Part V, Comm. Math. Phys. 5 (1967),

157-190; Part VI, Comm. Math. Phys. 6 (1967), 205-225.

20. R. Hermann, Formal linearization of a semisimple Lie algebra of vector fields about a singular point, Trans. Am. Math. Soc. 130 (1968), 105-109.

21. R. Hermann, A geometric formula for current algebra commutation relations, Phys. Rev. 177 (1969), 2449.

22. R. Hermann, Quantum field theories with degenerate Lagrangians, Phys. Rev. 177 (1969), 2453.

23. R. Hermann, Fourier Analysis on Groups and Partial Wave Analysis, W.A. Benjamin, New York, 1969.

24. R. Hermann, Algebraic and geometric structures in current algebra theory, ONR Technical Report No. 1., Institute for Advanced Study, Princeton, New Jersey, 1970.

25. R. Hermann, Current algebra, Sugawara model and differential geometry, J. Math. Phys. 11 (1970), 1825-1829.

26. R. Hermann, Infinite dimensional Lie algebra and current algebra, Proc. 1969 Battele-Seattl Recontres on Math. Physics, Springer-Verlag, Berlin, 1970, 312-337.

27. R. Hermann, Lie Algebras and Quantum Mechanics, W.A. Benjamin, New York, 1970.

28. R. Hermann, Vector Bundles in Mathematical Physics, Parts I & II, W.A. Benjamin, New York, 1870.

29. R. Hermann, Formal linearization of Lie algebras of vector fields near an invariant submanifold, J. Differential Geom. 1973.

30. R. Hermann, Spectrum-generating algebras in classical mechanics, I & II, J. Math Phys. 13 (1972), 833, 878.

31. R. Hermann, Left invariant geodesics and classical mechanics on manifolds, J. Math. Phys. 13 (1973), 460.

32. R. Hermann, Currents in classical field theories, J. Math. Phys. 13 (1972), 97.

33. R. Hermann, Lectures on Mathematical Physics, II, W.A. Benjamin, Reading, Mass., 1972.

34. R. Hermann, Geometry, Physics and Systems, Marcel Dekker, New York, 1973.

35. R. Hermann, Physical Aspects of Lie Group Theory, Univ. of Montreal Press, Montreal, 1974.

36. R. Hermann, Energy-Momentum Tensors, Vol. IV of Interdisciplinary Mathematics, Math Sci Press, Brookline, Mass., 1973.

37. R. Hermann, Topics in General Relativity, Vol. V of Interdisciplinary Mathematics, Math Sci Press, Brookline, Mass., 1973.

38. R. Hermann, Topics in the Mathematics of Quantum Mechanics, Vol. VI of Interdisciplinary Mathematics, Math Sci Press, Brookline, Mass., 1973.

39. R. Hermann, Associative Algebras, Spinors, Clifford and Cayley Algebra, Vol. VII of Interdisciplinary Mathematics, Math Sci Press, Brookline, Mass., 1974.

40. R. Hermann, Geometric Structure Theory of Systems-Control Theory and Physics, Part A, Vol. IX of Interdisciplinary Mathematics, Math Sci Press, Brookline, Mass., 1975.

41. R. Hermann, Gauge Fields and Cartan-Ehresmann Connections, Part A, Vol. X of Interdisciplinary Mathematics, Math Sci Press, Brookline, Mass., 1975.

42. R. Hermann, Geodesics of singular Riemannian metrics, Bull. Am. Math. Soc. 79 (1973), 780-782.

43. R. Hermann, Geometric Structure of Systems-Control Theory and Physics, Part B, Vol. XI of Interdisciplinary Mathematics, Math Sci Press, Brookline, Mass., 1976.

44. R. Hermann, Ricci and Levi-Civita's Tensor Analysis Paper, translation, comments and additional material by R. Hermann (Lie Groups: History, Frontiers and Applications, Vol. 2), Math Sci Press, 1975.

45. R. Hermann, 'Modern' differential geometry in elementary particle physics, VII GIFT Conference on Theoretical Physics, Salamonca, Spain, 1977, to appear in Proceedings, ed. by A. Azcárraga, published by Springer-Verlag.

46. R. Hermann, Quantum and Fermion Differential Geometry, Part A, Math Sci Press, Brookline, Mass., 1977.

47. R. Hermann, The differential geometry of foliations, Annals of Math. 72 (1960), pp. 445-457.

48. S. Kobayaski and K. Nomizu, Foundations of Differential Geometry, Wiley, 1962.

49. S. Sternberg, Minimal coupling and the symplectic mechanics of a classical particle in the presence of a Yang-Mills field, preprint, Tel-Aviv Univ., Tel-Aviv, Isreal.

50. J. D. Jackson, Classical Electrodynamics, Wiley, New York, 1962.

51. J. Dieudonné, Treatise of Analysis, Vol. 4, Academic Press, New York, 1974.

52. N. Steenrod, The Topology of Fiber Bundles, Princeton University Press, 1951.

Chapter II

THE GEOMETRY OF THE DIRAC MAGNETIC MONOPOLES, FIBER BUNDLES AND CONNECTIONS

1. INTRODUCTION

It has been recognized recently [1] that Dirac's magnetic monopole [2] is a beautiful example of fiber bundle-connection-holonomy ideas. In this chapter I will develop certain mathematical features that seem to be involved. I begin with a review, based on "Interdisciplinary Mathematics", Volume IV, and the standard physics reference for electromagnetism, Jackson's book [3].

2. HODGE'S *-OPERATOR FOR DIFFERENTIAL FORMS ON RIEMANNIAN MANIFOLDS

Let X be a Riemannian manifold. The Riemannian metric is initially given as an inner product

$$V_1, V_2 \to \langle V_1, V_2 \rangle$$

on vector fields $\mathcal{V}(X)$. (Do not assume it is positive, but suppose it is non-degenerate.) This sets up an isomorphism between $\mathcal{V}(X)$ and $\mathcal{D}^1(X)$. The inner product can then be transported over to $\mathcal{D}^1(X)$, where it is also denoted as $\langle\,,\rangle$. (Thus, it defines what I have called a *co-Riemannian metric*.) This inner product can now be extended to $\mathcal{D}^1(X)$. For example,

$$\langle \theta_1 \wedge \theta_2, \theta_1' \wedge \theta_2' \rangle = \langle \theta_1, \theta_1' \rangle \langle \theta_2, \theta_2' \rangle - \langle \theta_2, \theta_1' \rangle \langle \theta_1, \theta_2' \rangle$$

for $\theta_1, \theta_2 \in \mathcal{D}^1(X)$

Suppose $n = \dim X$. An *orientation* for X is the choice of an equivalence class of nonzero n-forms with $\omega \sim \omega'$ if $\omega' = f\omega'$ with $f(x) > 0$ for all x. Choose such an orientation. There is a unique n-form, called dx, such that:

a) dx is positively oriented

b) $\langle dx, dx \rangle = \pm 1$.

dx is called the *Riemannian volume element form.*

Definition. The Hodge *-operator is the linear map $\mathcal{D}^r(X) \to \mathcal{D}^{n-r}(S)$ satisfying the following conditions:

$$\theta \wedge (*\theta') = \langle \theta, \theta' \rangle dx \quad , \qquad \text{for } \theta, \theta' \in \mathcal{D}^r(X) \quad . \tag{2.1}$$

The Hodge operator is most readily written in terms of *orthonormal moving frames*. Let V_μ, $0 \le \mu,\nu \le n-1$, be a basis for $\mathcal{V}(X)$ which is *orthonormal* for the metric, i.e.,

$$g_{\mu\nu} = \langle V_\mu, V_\nu \rangle = \begin{cases} 0 & \text{if } \mu \neq \nu \\ \pm 1 & \text{if } \mu = \nu \end{cases} \tag{2.2}$$

Let θ^μ be the dual basis of one-forms, i.e.,

$$\theta^\mu(V_\nu) = \delta^\mu_\nu \quad . \tag{2.3}$$

Then,

$$\langle \theta^\mu, \theta^\nu \rangle = g^{\mu\nu} = g_{\mu\nu} = \langle V_\mu, V_\nu \rangle \tag{2.4}$$

Set:

$$dx = \theta^0 \wedge \cdots \wedge \theta^{n-1} \quad . \tag{2.5}$$

(Suppose the ordering of the vectors in the moving frame is chosen so that dx defined by (2.5) is positively oriented.) Then

$$\langle dx, dx \rangle = \pm 1 \tag{2.6}$$

dx is *the* Riemannian volume element form. Thus, if:

$$\omega = \theta^0 \quad ,$$

then

$$*\omega = \langle \theta^0, \theta^0 \rangle \, \theta^1 \wedge \cdots \wedge \theta^{n-1} \quad .$$

If $\omega = \theta^0 \wedge \theta^1$, then

$$*\omega = \langle \theta^0, \theta^0 \rangle \langle \theta^1, \theta^1 \rangle \, \theta^2 \wedge \cdots \wedge \theta^{n-1}$$

and so forth.

Theorem 2.1. Suppose that $X = R^3$ with Cartesian coordinates (x^i), $1 \le i,j \le 3$, and the Euclidean metric

$$ds^2 = dx^i \cdot dx^j \equiv \delta_{ij} dx^i dx^j$$

Then,

$$*(dx^i) = \varepsilon^i_{jk}\, dx^j \wedge dx^k \quad , \tag{2.7}$$

where (ε^i_{jk}) is the "Levi-Civita tensor", i.e., completely skew-symmetric in all indices, with

$$\varepsilon^1_{23} = 1 \quad .$$

<u>Proof</u>. Following the rules outlined above,

$$dx = dx^1 \wedge dx^2 \wedge dx^3$$

$$\langle dx^i, dx^j \rangle = \delta^{ij}$$

$$*(dx^1) = dx^2 \wedge dx^3$$

$$dx^2 \wedge *(dx^2) = dx$$

$$dx^1 \wedge (*dx^2) = 0 = dx^3 \wedge (*dx^2) \quad .$$

Hence,

$$*dx^2 = -dx^1 \wedge dx^3 \quad .$$

Similarly,

$$*dx^3 = dx^1 \wedge dx^2 \quad .$$

(2.7) follows.

Theorem 2.1 establishes the relation between the Hodge operation and traditional three-dimensional vector analysis.

$$*d\colon \mathscr{D}^1(R^3) \to \mathscr{D}^1(R^3)$$

is essentially "curl"

$$*d\colon \mathscr{D}^2(R^3) \to \mathscr{F}(R^3) \equiv \mathscr{D}^0(R^3)$$

is "divergence".

$$d\colon \mathscr{D}^0(R^3) \to \mathscr{D}^1(R^3)$$

is "gradient".

$\times \;=\; *\wedge \;\equiv\;$ vector product

$$\mathscr{D}^1(R^3) \times \mathscr{D}^1(R^3) \xrightarrow{\wedge} \mathscr{D}^2(R^3) \xrightarrow{*} \mathscr{D}^1(R^3) \quad .$$

3. MAXWELL'S EQUATIONS

Let us first write Maxwell's equations in the vector-analysis notation used in physics books (e.g., Jackson [3]).

$$\boxed{\begin{aligned} \frac{1}{c}\frac{\partial B}{\partial t} &= -\operatorname{curl} E \\ \frac{1}{c}\frac{\partial D}{\partial t} + 4\pi J &= \operatorname{curl} H \\ \operatorname{div} B &= 0 \\ \operatorname{div} D &= 4\pi\rho \\ \frac{\partial \rho}{\partial t} + \operatorname{div} J &= 0 \\ B &= \mu H \\ D &= \varepsilon E \end{aligned}} \tag{3.1}$$

Here B, D, E, H, J are time-dependent one-forms on R^3 (or, using the Euclidean metric to set up a correspondence between $\mathscr{V}(R^3)$ and $\mathscr{D}^1(R^3)$, time-dependent vector fields). Let (x^i) be Cartesian coordinates for R^3. Set:

$$E = E_i dx^i$$

$$B = B_i dx^i$$

$$D = D_i dx^i$$

$$H = H_i dx^i$$

$$J = J_i dx^i \quad .$$

Then, conditions (3.1) take the following form:

$$
\begin{array}{|rcl|}
\hline
d_3 * B & = & 0 \\
d_3 * D & = & 4\pi\rho dx \\
\frac{1}{c}\frac{\partial B}{\partial t} & = & * d_3 E \\
\frac{1}{c}\frac{\partial D}{\partial t} + 4\pi J & = & * d_3 H \\
\frac{\partial}{\partial t}(\rho dx) + d_3 * J & = & 0 \\
\hline
\end{array}
\qquad (3.2)
$$

Here d_3 denotes exterior derivative on the variables x^1, x^2, x^3, i.e., exterior derivative in R^3. (We shall also deal with exterior derivative in R^4 below.)

Consider R^4 as a manifold with coordinates

$$(t, x^1, x^2, x^3) \quad .$$

A two-form ω on R^4 can then be written in a unique way as

$$\omega = \alpha + \beta \wedge dt \quad , \tag{3.3}$$

where α is a two-form on R^3, i.e., in the variables (x^i), *with* t *as parameter*, and with β as a one-form in R^3, which depends on t as parameter. Then,

$$d\omega = d_3\alpha + \partial_t(\alpha) \wedge dt + d_3\beta \wedge dt \quad . \tag{3.4}$$

"d" denotes exterior derivative in R^4. In order to apply this formula, set:

$$F = \frac{1}{c} * B + E \wedge dt \tag{3.5}$$

$$F' = \frac{1}{c} * D - H \wedge dt \tag{3.6}$$

Then,

$$dF = \frac{1}{c} d_3 * B + \frac{1}{c} * \frac{\partial B}{\partial t} \wedge dt + d_3(E) \wedge dt$$

$$= \text{, using (3.2),}$$

$$0 \tag{3.7}$$

$$dF' = \frac{1}{c} d_3{*}D + \frac{1}{c}{*}\frac{\partial D}{\partial t} \wedge dt - d_3 H \wedge dt$$

$$= \text{, using (3.2),}$$

$$4\pi\rho dx - 4\pi J \wedge dt \qquad (3.8)$$

(3.7) and (3.8) are the usual Maxwell equations in the *four-dimensional format*. They do not, so far, involve the last two relations among the relations (3.1), the *constitutive relations*. If they are used, we have:

$$F' = \frac{\varepsilon}{c}{*}E - \frac{1}{\mu} B \wedge dt \quad .$$

If the μ, ε are constants, a metric can be defined on R^4 (reducing to the usual Minkowski metric if $\mu = \varepsilon = 1$) so that

$F' = {*}F \equiv$ Hodge dual of F with respect to this metric on R^4 .

4. THE "MAGNETIC CHARGE" IN FOUR-DIMENSIONAL NOTATION

In the Maxwell equations (3.1), let us simplify so that

$$\mu = \varepsilon = 1 \quad .$$

Only B and E remain independent, and we are left with the following simplified Maxwell equations:

$$\begin{aligned}
&\text{a)} \quad \operatorname{div} B = 0 \\
&\text{b)} \quad \operatorname{div} E = 4\pi\rho \\
&\text{c)} \quad \frac{1}{c}\frac{\partial B}{\partial t}{*} = -\operatorname{curl} E \\
&\text{d)} \quad \frac{1}{c}\frac{\partial E}{\partial t} + 4\pi J = \operatorname{curl} B \\
&\text{e)} \quad \frac{\partial \rho}{\partial t} + \dim J = 0
\end{aligned} \qquad (4.1)$$

Notice that "symmetry" between E and B in Equations (c) and (d) *if* J *is zero*:

$$B \to E \quad ; \quad E \to -B$$

Mathematically, this is analogous to the symmetry between position and momentum, i.e., q and p, in Hamilton's equations. For example, for the harmonic oscillator

$$h(q,p) = \frac{1}{2}(p^2 + q^2)$$

$$\frac{dq}{dt} = h_p \quad ; \quad \frac{dp}{dt} = -h_q \quad . \tag{4.2}$$

$(p \to q; \quad q \to -p)$ is a "symmetry", i.e., maps a solution into a solution. In fact, these are related, since Maxwell's equations with $J = 0$ represent an infinite number of harmonic oscillators. We can do the "particle" analogue of putting J back in by inserting a "force" into (4.2)

$$\frac{dp}{dt} = \frac{d^2q}{dt^2} = -q + f(t) = -h_q + f(t)$$

$$\frac{dp}{dt} = -h_q = -q \quad .$$

In scalar terms, we deal with

$$\frac{d^2q}{dt^2} + q = f(t)$$

and

$$\frac{d^2q}{dt^2} = -q + f''(t) \quad .$$

Analogously, Dirac tried to mathematically patch up the asymmetry between E and B in the inhomogeneous Maxwell equations by a similar trick. There has been extensive experimental search with no success, but it remains an interesting possibility. Notice how the four dimensional-differential form notation, (3.5) and (3.6), bring out this "symmetry" in an even more striking way. I will now show how Dirac's way of putting in "magnetic charge" and current ρ_m, δ_m is interpreted in the four-dimensional notation. First, I do it in the usual three-dimensional way:

$$
\begin{aligned}
\operatorname{div} B &= 4\pi\rho_m \\
\operatorname{div} E &= 4\pi\rho_e \\
\frac{1}{c}\frac{\partial B}{\partial t} + \operatorname{curl} E &= -4\pi J_m \\
\frac{1}{c}\frac{\partial E}{\partial t} - \operatorname{curl} B &= -4\pi J_e \\
\frac{\partial \rho_m}{\partial t} + \operatorname{dim} J_m &= 0 \\
\frac{\partial \rho_e}{\partial t} + \operatorname{dim} J_e &= 0
\end{aligned}
\tag{4.2}
$$

We can again set:

$$
\begin{aligned}
F &= \frac{1}{c} * B + E \wedge dt \\
F' &= \frac{1}{c} * E - B \wedge dt
\end{aligned}
\tag{4.3}
$$

Calculating in the same way as in Section 3, we see that Equations (4.2) are equivalent to the following:

$$
\begin{aligned}
\text{a)}\quad dF &= 4\pi(\rho_m dx - J_m \wedge dt) \\
\text{b)}\quad dF' &= 4\pi(\rho_e dx - J_e \wedge dt)
\end{aligned}
\tag{4.4}
$$

Put together with the equation

$$F' = *F \quad ,$$

this puts Dirac's theory squarely within the theory of "currents" created by G. deRham [4]. It would, in fact, be very interesting and important to look at it from this point of view (which apparently has never been done systematically). However, our concern here is the relation between these equations and the theory of *fiber bundles*.

Suppose the right hand side of (4.4a) is zero on an open subset X of R^4. One can then construct a line bundle with a connection on X (e.g., using Kaluza-Klein so that F is essentially the *curvature* of this connection.) The presence of the "magnetic charge and current" on the right hand side of (4.4) will then manifest itself in the presence of some sort of *singularity* of this (bundle + connection) in the set $R^4 - X$. It is this geometry that we will study here.

Remark. This very much falls within the general domain of an idea of Einstein's:

> "Particles" are to be *defined* as "singularities" of "fields", i.e., of *geometric objects*.

As far as I know, this relation has not been pursued in any systematic way. This is extremely depressing for a mathematician to see, and bears out my personal hypothesis that one of the causes of the physicists' muddle in elementary particle theory is their rejection of the sort of *general* insight that *good* mathematics might give them if they did not spend all their time simultaneously fighting it off and rewriting it themselves. Thus, there is extensive work by the Relativists on the singularities of a Riemannian metric, i.e., a gravitational field. Algebraic geometry also has a good deal to say about the structure of singularities of *bundles*. I suspect that the Dirac problem is a hybrid of this question and the one encountered in relativity. Finally, note that the "Kaluza-Klein" viewpoint I am developing relates the two even more intimately--Riemannian metrics have *geodesics*, "completeness" and "incompleteness" *makes sense*, and gives one a superb geometric language with which to think about these problems.

Before getting into these "global" questions, I want to return to local differential geometry in order to clarify the relation between the Hodge $\star$-operator and the divergence operation.

5. THE DIVERGENCE AND THE HODGE-DUAL OF EXTERIOR DERIVATIVE

The *divergence* of a tensor field is a basic operation in classical tensor analysis, and plays a widespread role in expressing the "laws of physics" in geometric form. (Recall that this possibility was one of the foremost ideas in Einstein's mind in his search for unified geometric descriptions of physical phenomena.) Thus, in tensor analysis language, Maxwell's equations take the form:

$$\text{a)}\quad F_{\mu\nu,\omega} - F_{\mu\omega,\nu} - F_{\omega\nu,\mu} = 0$$

$$\text{b)}\quad g^{\nu\omega} F_{\mu\nu,\omega} = J_\mu \qquad (5.1)$$

(5.1a) expresses the fact that

$$dF = 0 \quad , \qquad (5.2)$$

where

$$F = F_{\mu\nu} dx^\mu \wedge dx^\nu \qquad (5.3)$$

while (5.1b) can also be written in Hodge form as

$$*d*F = J \equiv J_\mu dx^\mu \quad . \qquad (5.4)$$

Now, it is not obvious that the tensor analysis "divergence" operation is identical with (5.4), and I want to explore the (basically algebraic) reasons for this a bit more clearly.

Let X be a manifold with a Riemannian metric $<,>$ as an inner product on both tangent vectors and differential forms. Fix an orientation and let dx be the corresponding Riemannian volume element form. Suppose $n = \dim X$ so that dx is an n-form. The Hodge $*$-operator is then defined as follows:

$$\theta \wedge *\theta' = <\theta,\theta'> dx \qquad (5.5)$$

$$\text{for } \theta,\theta' \in \mathcal{D}^r(X) \quad .$$

We want to compute the operator

$$\delta = *dx \quad . \qquad (5.6)$$

It is called the *Hodge dual* of d. (It plays the key role in Hodge's theory of "Harmonic Integrals" [4,5], which is one of the foremost accomplishments of 20-th century mathematics. It can also be considered the "Hilbert space dual" when appropriate Hilbert space norms are chosen for the differential forms.)

As a first step, let us compute

$$*(\theta_1 \wedge \theta_2)$$

where θ_1 is a one-form and θ_2 is an $(r-1)$-form. Using (5.5)

$$\theta' \wedge *(\theta_1 \wedge \theta_2) = <\theta',\theta_1 \wedge \theta_2> dx \qquad (5.7)$$

$$\text{for all } \theta' \in \mathcal{D}^r(X) \quad .$$

Let V be the isomorphic image of θ, in $\mathscr{V}(X)$ (in the isomorphism between $\mathscr{D}^1(X)$ and $\mathscr{V}(X)$ set up by the metric), i.e.,

$$\langle\theta,\omega\rangle = \omega(\mathscr{V}) .$$

for all $\omega \in \mathscr{D}^1(X)$.

Then,

$$\begin{aligned}\langle\omega_1 \wedge \cdots \omega_r, \theta_1 \wedge \theta_2\rangle &= \langle\theta_1,\omega_1\rangle \langle\theta_2, \omega_2 \wedge \cdots \wedge \omega_r\rangle \\ &\quad - \langle\theta_1,\omega_2\rangle \langle\theta_2, \omega_1 \wedge \omega_3 \wedge \cdots \wedge \omega_r\rangle + \cdots \\ &= (V \lrcorner \omega_1) \langle\theta_2, \omega_2 \wedge \cdots \wedge \omega_r\rangle \\ &\quad - (V \lrcorner \omega_2) \langle\theta_2, \omega_1 \wedge \omega_3 \wedge \cdots \wedge \omega_r\rangle + \cdots \\ &= \langle V \lrcorner (\omega_1 \wedge \cdots \wedge \omega_r), \theta_2\rangle\end{aligned}$$

This gives another basic formula:

$$\langle\theta', \theta_1 \wedge \theta_2\rangle = \langle V \lrcorner \theta', \theta_2\rangle \tag{5.8}$$

Apply (5.8) in (5.7):

$$\begin{aligned}\theta' \wedge (\theta_1 \wedge \theta_2) &= \langle V \lrcorner \theta', \theta_2\rangle \, dx \\ &= (V \lrcorner \theta') \wedge *\theta_2 \\ &= (-1)^{r+1} \theta' \wedge (V \lrcorner *\theta_2) ,\end{aligned}$$

or

$$\boxed{*(\theta_1 \wedge \theta_2) = (-1)^{r+1} V \lrcorner *\theta_2} \tag{5.9}$$

for $\theta_1 \in \mathscr{D}^1(X)$, $\theta_2 \in \mathscr{D}^{r-1}(X)$.

Thus, for $f \in \mathscr{F}(X)$, $\theta \in \mathscr{D}^r(X)$,

$$\begin{aligned}\delta(f\theta) &= *d*(f\theta) \\ &= *df*\theta \\ &= *(df \wedge (*\theta)) + *df*\theta\end{aligned}$$

$$= *(df \wedge *\theta) + f\delta\theta$$

$= $, using (5.9)

$$(-1)^{n-r+1}(\text{grad } f) \lrcorner **(\theta) + f\delta\theta$$

$$= \pm (\text{grad } f \lrcorner \theta) + f\delta\theta \tag{5.10}$$

Remark. This formula essentially computes the "symbol" of the linear differential operator δ. See my book, Geometry, Physics and Systems.

We can now use (5.10) to compute $\delta\theta$, for an arbitrary one-form, in terms of *moving frames*. Let (ω^μ), $0 \leq \mu,\nu \leq n-1$, be an orthornormal basis for one-forms,

$$\langle\omega^\mu,\omega^\nu\rangle = g^{\mu\nu} \equiv \text{constants} \quad .$$

At each point $x_0 \in X$, we can choose ω^μ so that

$$d\omega^\mu(x_0) = 0 \quad .$$

Suppose

$$\theta = a_{\mu_1 \cdots \mu_r} \omega^{\mu_1} \wedge \cdots \wedge \omega^{\mu_r} \tag{5.11}$$

at x_0,

$$\delta\theta = \pm g^{\mu\nu} a_{\mu_1 \cdots \mu_r,\mu} \left(V_\nu \lrcorner \left(\omega^{\mu_1} \wedge \cdots \wedge \omega^{\mu_r}\right)\right) \tag{5.12}$$

where

$$da_{\mu_1 \cdots \mu_2} = a_{\mu_1 \cdots \mu_{r,\mu}} \omega^\mu \quad ,$$

$$V_\mu(\omega^\nu) = \delta^\nu_\mu$$

(5.12) now holds at all points of X, providing that one interprets the comma before μ as the *covariant derivative*, in the sense of tensor analysis. It is then the definitve "differential-geometric" version of the formula for δ.

Specialize (5.12): $r = 1$

$$\delta\theta = g^{\mu\nu} a_{\nu,\mu}$$

$$= \pm\frac{1}{2} g^{\mu\nu} (a_{\nu,\mu} + a_{\mu,\nu})$$

The isomorphic vector field V to θ then is a *Killing vector field* if $\delta\theta = 0$.

<u>n = 2</u>

$$\delta\theta = \pm g^{\mu\nu} a_{\mu_1\mu_2,\nu} V_\nu \lrcorner \left(\omega^{\mu_1} \wedge \omega^{\mu_2}\right)$$

$$= \pm\left(g^{\mu\mu_1} a_{\mu_1\mu_2,\mu} \omega^{\mu_2} - g^{\mu\mu_2} a_{\mu_1\mu_2,\mu} \omega^{\mu_1}\right)$$

$$= \pm\left(g^{\mu\mu_1}\left(2a_{\mu_1\mu_2,\mu} \omega^{\mu_2}\right)\right)$$

$$= \pm 2g^{\mu\mu_1} a_{\mu_1\nu,\mu} \omega^{\nu}$$

This shows that $\delta\theta$ is, in tensor analysis (up to a constant) just the *divergence*.

6. PRINCIPAL BUNDLES WITH LIE GROUPS AS STRUCTURE GROUP AND THEIR ASSOCIATED FIBER BUNDLES

Let us now return to the study of the geometry of the magnetic monopole. The topic mentioned in the title to this section is a standard concept in differential geometry [6-8], and is one key to making precise the "global" nature of Dirac's argument.

<u>Definition</u>. *A principal fiber bundle with structure group* G is determined by the following data:

a) A pair (Y,X) of manifolds with an onto map $\pi: Y \to X$ which is a submersion
b) A Lie group G
c) An action of G on Y such that:
d) The orbits of G are the fibers of π, and
e) $gy = y$ for $g \in G$, since $y \in Y \Rightarrow g =$ identity

<u>Definition</u>. Let (G,π,Y,X) be a principal fiber bundle with structure group G. Let F be another space, together with a transformation group action of G on F. Let G act on the product $Y \times F$ via the diagonal action

$$g(y,f) = (gy,gf) \quad .$$

The orbit space $Y_F \equiv G\backslash(Y \times F)$ is called the *associated fiber bundle with fiber isomorphism to* F. Map $Y_F \to X$ as follows to make it a fiber space over X:

$$\pi_F\colon \overline{(y,f)} \to \pi(x)$$

Let us compute the fibers of π_F. If $(y,t) \in Y \times F$, denote by $\overline{(y,f)}$ the orbit of G on which it lies. Now, suppose that $\overline{(y,f)}$ and $\overline{(y',f')}$ lie in the same fiber of π_F. This means that

$$\pi(y) = y' ,$$

i.e., that there is a $g \in G$ such that

$$y' = gy .$$

Let $x \in X$. *Pick a point* $y \in \pi^{-1}(x)$. Map $F \to \pi_F^{-1}(x)$ as follows

$$f \to \overline{(y,f)} = \phi_y(f) \tag{6.1}$$

<u>Theorem 6.1</u>. For each $y \in \pi^{-1}(x)$, the map $\phi_y\colon F \to \pi_F^{-1}(x)$ is one-one and onto.

<u>Proof</u>. To prove it is onto, suppose $\overline{(y',f')} \in \pi_F^{-1}(x)$, i.e.,

$$\overline{(y,u)},\ \overline{(y',t')}$$

lie on the same fiber. As we remarked above,

$$y' = gy .$$

Hence,

$$\begin{aligned} g^{-1}\overline{(y',f')} &= \overline{(y',f')} \\ &= \overline{(g^{-1},y',g^{-'},f')} \\ &= \overline{(y,g^{-1}f')} \\ &= \phi_y(g^{-1}f') \end{aligned}$$

This proves that ϕ_y is onto.

Let us prove that ϕ_y is one-one. Suppose

$$\phi_y(f) = \phi_y(f') ,$$

i.e.,

$$\overline{(y,f)} = \overline{(y,f')}$$

i.e.,

$$(y,f') = g(y,f)$$

for some $g \in G$,

$$y = gy \tag{6.2}$$

and

$$f' = gf \quad .$$

(6.2) now forces $g \equiv$ identity. (This is one of the postulates defining the "principal fiber bundle" concept.) Hence,

$$f' = f \quad ,$$

which shows that ϕ_y is one-one.

Remark. Notice that ϕ_y does *not* intertwine the action of G since G does not act naturally on $Y_F \equiv G\backslash(Y \times F)$.

We can now sum up as follows:

Theorem 6.2. The space $Y_F \equiv G\backslash(Y \times F)$ forms a fiber space over X. The fibers are all isomorphic to F, although there is no "uniquely determined" isomorphism.

One can also show that this contribution is "natural" from the point of view of manifold theory, i.e., Y_f admits a manifold structure, π_F is a submersion, etc. One way to do this is to remark that G acts freely and "totally discontinuously" on $Y \times F$, hence its orbit space admits a natural manifold structure.

The construction of this space Y_F is a basic one in differential geometry. As we shall see below, it is an abstract version of the construction a physicist makes every time he constructs "tensorial" or "spinorial" fields.

7. CROSS-SECTION OF THE ASSOCIATED FIBER SPACES AS "COVARIANTS" OF THE STRUCTURE GROUP

If $\pi: E \to X$ is a fiber space over a manifold, the space of cross-section maps

$$\Gamma(E) = \{\psi: X \to E: \pi\psi = \text{identity}\}$$

is a basic object of great interest to both physicists and mathematicians. In case the fiber space is constructed via the "associated bundle" construction given in Section 6, we can give an extremely useful alternate description of $\Gamma(E)$.

Suppose then that (π,Y,X,G) is a principal fiber bundle with structure group G. Let F be another space on which G acts as a transformation group. Let G act on $Y \times F$. The orbit space $G\backslash(Y \times F)$ is then $Y_F \equiv E$, the associated bundle.

Consider a map

$$\psi: Y \to F$$

which *intertwines* the action of G, i.e., satisfies the following condition

$$\psi(gy) = g\psi(y) \qquad (7.1)$$

$$\text{for } g \in G, \ y \in Y \quad .$$

Associate with ψ its *graph*, denoted by $\text{gr}(\psi)$. It is a map $Y \to Y \times F$

$$\text{gr}(\psi)(y) = (y,\psi(y)) \qquad . \qquad (7.2)$$

We can follow it with the projection

$$Y \times F \to G\backslash(Y \times F) \quad ,$$

obtaining a map: $Y \to Y_F$ that we denote as $\overline{\text{gr}(\psi)}$. Write the diagram of mapping

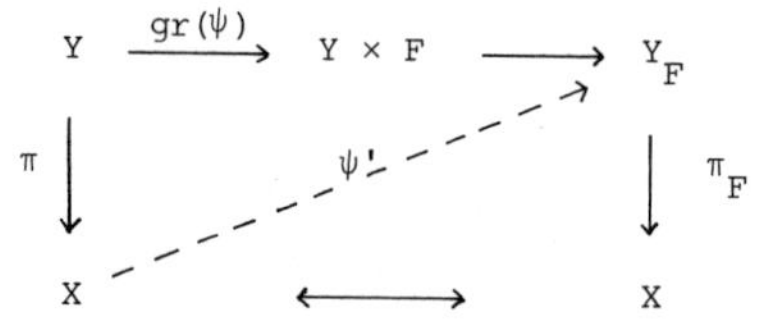

$$\begin{array}{ccccc}
Y & \xrightarrow{\text{gr}(\psi)} & Y \times F & \longrightarrow & Y_F \\
\pi \downarrow & & \psi' \nearrow & & \downarrow \pi_F \\
X & & \longleftrightarrow & & X
\end{array} \qquad (7.3)$$

We see from (7.6) that this diagram of mappings is *commutative*. Can we now find a mapping

$$\psi': X \to Y_F$$

which preserves the commutativity of the diagram (7.3) when it is inserted? If it exists, it will obviously be a cross-section, i.e.,

$$\pi_F \psi' = \text{identity} \quad .$$

The existence of ψ' means that

$$\overline{(\text{gr } \psi)} \text{ maps each fiber of } \pi \text{ into a point of } Y_F \quad . \qquad (7.4)$$

Conversely, condition (7.4) guarantees the existence of ψ'. Let us then check whether (7.4) is satisfied. Suppose that y,y' are two points in the fiber of π. Since (π,Y,X) is a *principal* bundle, this means that there is a $g \in G$ such that

$$y' = gy \quad .$$

Thus,

$$\begin{aligned} gr(\psi)(y') &= (y',\psi(y')) \\ &= (gy,\psi(gy)) \\ &= \text{, using the intertwining property (7.1),} \\ &\quad (gy,g\psi(y)) \\ &= g(y,\psi(y)) \end{aligned}$$

Hence,

$$\overline{gr(\psi)}(y') = \overline{(y,\psi(y))} \quad ,$$

which proves (7.4).

We can now sum up as follows.

Theorem 7.1. The space $\Gamma(Y_F)$ of cross-sections of the associated bundle is identified with the space of intertwining maps: $Y \to F$.

(The completion of the proof involves retracing the argument to show that conversely each cross-section comes in this way from an intertwining map.)

We will see that this identification is a key feature in the theory of "induced representations" of Lie groups. It is also the key to seeing the meaning of "tensorial fields" and "spinorial fields" (and the difference between them!)

8. VECTOR BUNDLES

Keep the notation of Section 7. Specialize the action of G on F to be a *linear* action. This means that F is a vector space, hence we will change the notation and call it "V". The field of scalars of this vector space may be arbitrary, but for geometric purposes it suffices to consider it as the real or complex numbers.

Let $L(V)$ denote the space of linear maps $V \to V$. Suppose given a *linear representation of* G on V, i.e., a homomorphism

$$\sigma: G \to L(V) \quad .$$

Define the transformation group action of G on V as follows:

$$(g,v) \to gv = \sigma(g)(v) \quad .$$

The construction

$$Y_\sigma = G\backslash(Y \times V)$$

thus provides a fiber space over X with each fiber isomorphic to V. Although these isomorphisms are not unique, each preserves the linear structure, i.e., the *fibers* of $Y_\sigma \to X$ can be given vector space structures, i.e.,

$$\pi_\sigma: Y_\sigma \to X$$

is a *vector bundle*. $\Gamma(Y_\sigma)$, the space of cross-sections, is then identified with the space of maps

$$\psi: Y \to V$$

such that

$$\psi(gy) = \sigma(g^{-1})\psi(y) \tag{8.1}$$

for all $g \in G$, $y \in Y$.

Two such maps can be added (since V is a vector space), thus exhibiting the "natural" vector space structure for $\Gamma(Y_\sigma)$.

9. TENSORIAL FIELDS AND THE PRINCIPAL TANGENT FRAME BUNDLE TO A MANIFOLD

Let X be a manifold, x a point of X. X_x denotes the tangent space to X at x. Suppose that X is m-dimensional. Recall that X_x is an m-dimensional real vector space. A *basis* for X_x, i.e., an m-tuple

$$\underline{v} = (v_1,\ldots,v_m)$$

(that we write as a row vector for convenient calculation) of elements of X_x which are linearly independent. Such a basis is geometrically called the *tangent frame*. Y, the *principal frame bundle* to X, is defined as the set of all such tangent frames, i.e., an element of Y is a pair

$$(x,\underline{v})$$

with $x \in X$, $\underline{v}$ a tangent frame at x. The fiber space map $\pi: Y \to X$ is defined as

$$\pi(x,\underline{v}) = x \quad .$$

Let G be the group $GL(m,R)$, i.e., the group of $m \times m$ real matrices of nonzero determinant. Given

$$g = \begin{pmatrix} g_{11} & g_{12} & \cdots & g_{1m} \\ \vdots & & & \\ g_{m1} & & \cdots & g_{mm} \end{pmatrix}$$

let it act on the tangent frame $\underline{v}$ (considered as a *row* vector) via the usual rule for matrix multiplication

$$(g,\underline{v}) \to \underline{v}g^{-1} \quad . \tag{9.2}$$

This rule makes Y into a *principal* $GL(m,R)$*-bundle*.

Let Z be R^m, and let

$$\sigma: G \to L(Z)$$

be the "natural" representation of G, i.e., if

$$z = \begin{pmatrix} z_1 \\ \vdots \\ z_m \end{pmatrix}$$

is an element of R^m, then

$$g = \begin{pmatrix} g_{11} & \cdots & g_{1m} \\ \vdots & & \\ g_{m1} & \cdots & g_{mm} \end{pmatrix}$$

then

$$gz = \begin{pmatrix} g_{11} & \cdots & g_{1m} \\ \vdots & & \\ g_{m1} & \cdots & g_{mm} \end{pmatrix} \begin{pmatrix} z_1 \\ \vdots \\ z_m \end{pmatrix}$$

Let $T(X)$ denote the tangent bundle to X. Map

$$\alpha: Y \times Z \to T(X)$$

as follows:

$$\alpha((x,\underline{v}),z) = \underline{v}z$$

$$= (v_1,\dots,v_m)\begin{pmatrix} z_1 \\ \vdots \\ z_m \end{pmatrix}$$

$$= z_1v_1 + \cdots + z_mv_m$$

Notice that

$$\alpha(g(x,\underline{v})) = \alpha(x,\underline{v})$$

for all $g \in GL(m,R)$,

i.e., α "passes to the quotient" to define a map

$$\overline{\alpha}: Y_\sigma \equiv G\backslash(Y \times Z) \to T(X)$$

Theorem 9.1. $\overline{\alpha}$ defines a vector bundle isomorphism, i.e., the vector bundle associated with the "basic" representation σ of $G = GL(m,R)$ is the *tangent bundle* to X.

The proof involves checking the definitions.

We can now choose other linear representations of GL(m,R) to define more general "tensors". For example, consider σ^d, the "dual" to the basic representation. The associated bundle is $T^d(X)$, the *cotangent bundle*. All other (finite dimensional) linear representations of GL(m,R) are built up out of tensor products"

$$\underbrace{\sigma \otimes \dots \otimes \sigma}_{\text{p copies}} \otimes \underbrace{\sigma^d \otimes \cdots \otimes \sigma^d}_{\text{q copies}}$$

Of course, these are not *irreducible*. Splitting up into irreducible components, i.e., finding "irreducible tensors", involves applying the "symmetrizing operators" defined by "Young diagrams".

This description of "tensor fields" is very consistent with classical "tensor analysis". A *tensor field* is defined by assigning to each moving frame

$$(x,\underline{v})$$

an n-tuple

$$\underline{\tau} = (\tau_1,\dots,\tau_n)$$

of real numbers, such that its components change in a *linear homogeneous* way when the basis $(v_1,\ldots,v_m)$ for tangent vectors is chosen. We shall now see that it leads very naturally to the generalization to "spinor fields".

10. SPINOR FIELDS

Let X now be a *Riemannian* manifold. This means that at every point $x \in X$ there is a non-degenerate, symmetric bilinear form $\langle\, , \rangle$ on X_x. Suppose its canonical form has p plus signs and q minus signs, so that the group of linear isomorphisms of X_x preserving the form is essentially the matrix group $O(p,q)$. An *orthonormal frame* at $x \in X$ is a basis

$$\underline{v} = (v_1,\ldots,v_m)$$

for X_x such that:

$$\langle v_i, v_j \rangle = \begin{cases} \delta_{ij} & \text{for } 1 \le i,j \le p \\ -\delta_{ij} & \text{for } p+1 \le i,j \le q \\ 0 & \text{if } i \neq j \end{cases}$$

Y, the *principal frame bundle* for the Riemannian metric, is defined as the set of such pairs $(x,\underline{v})$. $G \equiv O(p,q)$ acts on it as before.

$$g(x,\underline{v}) = (x,\underline{v}g^{-1}) \quad .$$

Let G' be the two-fold covering group of $O(p,q)$ called the *spinor group*. Let

$$\sigma\colon G' \to L(V)$$

be a linear representation of G' as a vector space V.

A *spinorial field* is now a mapping

$$\psi\colon Y \to V$$

such that:

$$\psi(gy) = \sigma(g)\psi(y)$$

$$\text{for } y \in Y, \quad g \in G \quad .$$

These spinor fields are *not* cross-sections of a vector bundle over X except if a certain Stiefel-Whitney characteristic class vanishes.

11. HOMOGENEOUS VECTOR BUNDLES ON HOMOGENEOUS SPACES. INDUCED REPRESENTATIONS

The "associated bundle" construction given above is the basis for all of differential geometry and physics. It is also fundamental for group representation theory, as I will now indicate.

Let L be a Lie group and let G be a closed subgroup. Regard G as a transformation group on L by using the *right* multiplication.

$$g(\ell) = \ell g^{-1} \tag{11.1}$$

for $g \in G$, $\ell \in L$.

The orbit space

$$G\backslash L$$

is then the coset space G/L. L is then a principal bundle over $G/L = X$, with G as structure group.

Let $\sigma: G \to L(V)$ be a linear representation of G on a vector space V. It determines a vector bundle

$$E_\sigma = G\backslash(L \times V)$$

with fiber isomorphic to V. A cross-section $\psi: X \to E_\sigma$ is then determined as a map

$$L \to V$$

such that

$$\psi(g(\ell)) = \sigma(g^{-1})\psi(\ell) \quad .$$

In view of (11.1), this means that

$$\psi(g\ell) = \sigma(\ell^{-1})\psi(g) \quad . \tag{11.2}$$

Let Γ_σ denote the set of all ψ satisfying (11.2). There is a representation

$$\rho_\sigma: L \to L(\Gamma_\sigma)$$

defined as follows:

$$\rho(\ell)(\psi)(\ell_1) = \psi(\ell^{-1}\ell_1)$$

ρ_σ is called the *representation of* L *induced from the representation of* σ. See my Lie Groups for Physicists for a brief account. (Unfortunately, there is no complete and systematic account of the *geometric* theory of induced representations in the literature. I plan to provide one some day!)

12. EHRESMANN CONNECTIONS IN ASSOCIATED FIBER BUNDLES

Given a principal G-bundle

$$\pi: Y \to X \tag{12.1}$$

and a space F on which G acts as a transformation group, we can define the *associated* fiber bundle Y_F as the orbit space

$$G\backslash(Y \times F) \quad .$$

An Ehresmann connection for (12.1) which is G-*covariant* will define an Ehresmann connection for $Y_F \to X$ by the mechanism we shall now explain. An *Ehresmann connection* for the fiber space (12.1) may be defined as a field

$$y \to H_y$$

of linear subspaces of $T(Y)$ such that

$$Y_g = \pi_*^{-1}(0) \oplus H_y \tag{12.2}$$

$$\text{for all } y \in Y \quad .$$

Let us suppose it is G-*invariant*, i.e.,

$$g_*(H_y) = H_{gy} \tag{12.3}$$

$$\text{for all } g \in G, \ y \in Y \quad .$$

$Y \times F$ can be considered as a fiber bundle over X. Map

$$(y,t) \to \pi(y) \quad . \tag{12.4}$$

Define $H'_{(y,t)}$ as $\iota_*(H_y)$, where

$$\iota: Y \to (y,t) \tag{12.5}$$

is the inclusion map. This defines H' as an Ehresmann connection for the fiber space (12.4). Consider the projection

$$\phi: Y \times F \to G\backslash(Y \times F) \equiv Y_F \quad .$$

G acting on $Y \times F$ preserves H', hence H' projects down under ϕ to define a field H" of tangent subspaces to Y_F, i.e.,

$$\phi_*(H'_{(y,f)}) = H''_{\phi(y,f)}$$

H" defines the Ehresmann connection for the fiber space $Y_F \to X$.

13. LINEAR CONNECTIONS IN ASSOCIATED VECTOR BUNDLES DEFINED BY EHRESMANN CONNECTIONS IN PRINCIPAL BUNDLES

The immediate point for physics of all this formalism is that it will give a way of describing "intrinsically" the basic operation in Dirac's monopole paper [2], passing from an electromagnetic field as the curvature of an Ehresmann connection in a principal SO(2,R) -bundle to the "Schrödinger equation" for a "quantum" charged particle interacting with a *classical* electromagnetic field. (In fact, the *global* existence of a global SO(2,R)-bundle *together* with an SO(2,R)-invariant connection is what determines Dirac's "quantization" condition!)

Let $\pi: E \to X$ be a vector bundle (with real vector spaces as fibers) over a manifold X. Let $\Gamma(E)$ denote the space of cross-section maps $\psi: X \to E$. $\Gamma(E)$ is an $\mathcal{F}(X)$-module. A (linear) *connection* for E is an R-linear map

$$\mathcal{V}(X) \times \Gamma(E) \to \Gamma(E)$$

$$(X,\gamma) \to \nabla_X\gamma$$

such that

$$\nabla_{fV}\gamma = f\nabla_V\gamma$$
$$\nabla_V(f\gamma) = V(f)\gamma + f\nabla_V\gamma \qquad (13.1)$$

for $f \in \mathcal{F}(X)$, $v \in \mathcal{V}(X)$, $\gamma \in \Gamma(X)$.

Let us see how an Ehresmann connection for $E \to X$ can define a linear connection. Suppose given an Ehresmann connection, i.e., a field

$$e \to H_e$$

of tangent subspaces to H such that

$$E_e = \pi_*^{-1}(0) \oplus H_e \qquad (13.2)$$

for all $e \in E$.

Given a vector field $V \in \mathcal{V}(X)$, there is a *horizontal lifting*, i.e., a vector field V_H on E such that:

$$V_H(e) \in H_e \text{ for all } e \in E \qquad (13.3)$$

$$\pi^*(V(f)) = V_H(\pi^*(f)) \qquad (13.4)$$

for all $f \in \mathcal{F}(X)$

Remark. Alternately, condition (13.4) can be written in any one of the following forms:

$$\pi_*(V_H(e)) = V(\pi(e)) \tag{13.5}$$

for all $e \in E$.

$$\pi_*(V_H) = V . \tag{13.6}$$

π maps an orbit curve of V_H onto an orbit curve of V. (13.7)

Now, let

$t \to \exp(tV_H)$

$t \to \exp(tV)$

be the one-parameter groups of diffeomorphisms of E and X generated by V and V_H. Conditions (13.4) - (13.7) mean that:

$$\pi \exp(tV_H)e = \exp(tV)\pi e , \tag{13.8}$$

i.e., π intertwines the action of these groups. From the geometric meaning of "parallel transport", we see that:

> Suppose $t \to \exp(tV)(x)$ is an orbit curve of V on the base, with $x_1 = \exp(V)(x)$ Then $\exp(V_H)$ maps $\pi^{-1}(x)$ onto $\pi^{-1}(x_1)$ and is the *parallel transport* defined by the Ehresmann connection.

Definition. The Ehresmann connection H is *linear* if each $\exp(V_H)$ maps fibers of π *linearly*, i.e., if parallel transport along curve in the base is always *linear*.

Now, given such a linear Ehresmann connection, we can define an covariant derivative operation satisfying (13.1). Given $\gamma \in \Gamma(E)$, $t \in R$, $V \in \mathcal{V}(X)$,

$$\exp(tV_H)\gamma \exp(-tV) \equiv \gamma_t \tag{13.9}$$

is again a cross-section of E.

Proof. To say that γ_t is a cross-section is to say that

$$\gamma_t^* \pi^*(f) = f \tag{13.10}$$

for all $f \in \mathscr{F}(X)$.

Now, using (13.9),

$$\begin{aligned}\gamma_t^* \pi^*(f) &= \exp(-tV)^* \gamma^* \exp(tV_H)^* \pi^*(f) \\ &= \exp(-t\gamma)^* \gamma^* \pi^* \exp(tV)^*(f) \\ &= \exp(-tV)^* (\pi\gamma)^* \exp(tV)^*(f) \\ &= \exp(-tV)^* \exp(tV)^*(f) \\ &= f\end{aligned}$$

whence (13.10).

Definition. The *covariant derivative* of γ by $V \in \mathscr{V}(X)$, $\nabla_V \gamma$, is defined as follows:

$$\nabla_V \gamma = \frac{\partial}{\partial t} \gamma_t \bigg|_{t=0} , \tag{13.11}$$

i.e., $\gamma \to \nabla_V \gamma$ is the negative of the infinitesimal generator of the one-parameter *linear* group

$$\alpha_t : \gamma \to \exp(tV_H) \gamma \exp(-tV) \equiv \gamma_t$$

acting in $\Gamma(E)$.

It is left to the reader as an exercise to show that (13.1) is now satisfied--it follows directly from the formalism. We now jump to the main physical application.

14. THE ELECTROMAGNETIC FIELD AS A LINEAR U(1)-CONNECTION AND AS A COVARIANT DERIVATIVE OPERATION IN THE SCHRÖDINGER WAVE-FUNCTION VECTOR BUNDLE

Now specialize the notation of Section 13 as follows:

$$X = R^4, \text{ Minkowski space-time}$$

$$Y = X \times \mathbb{C}$$

Denote a point of Y as (x,z), $x \in X$, $z \in \mathbb{C}$. The fiber space projection

$\pi: Y \to X$ is $(x,z) \to x$. Γ, the space of cross-section maps, consists of the maps of the form

$$\gamma: x \to (x,\psi(x)) \tag{14.1}$$

with $\psi: X \to \mathbb{C}$.

Let (x^μ), $0 \le \mu,\nu \le 3$, be the usual coordinates of relativistic physics, i.e.,

$$x^0 = \text{time}$$

$$x^1,x^2,x^3 = \text{space coordinates.}$$

Assume that all the adjustable constants of electromagnetism (e.g., the velocity of light) are equal to one.

The fiber space (π,Y,X) is a *vector bundle* with a one-dimensional complex vector space as fiber. (It is also called a *line bundle*.) A *linear Ehresmann connection* (i.e., a field of horizontal tangent spaces whose parallel transport preserves the linear structure on the fibers) may be defined by a one-form

$$\theta = dz - iA_\mu(x)z dx^\mu$$

(The tangent vectors $v \in T(Y)$ such that $\theta(v) = 0$ are the *horizontal* ones.) If the $A_\mu(x)$ are *real* functions, then the parallel transport preserves the norm $|z|^2 = z\bar{z}$, i.e., the structure group is $U(1) = SO(2,R)$. (We shall see below how this connection may also be associated with an invariant connection in a principal bundle with $U(1)$ as structure group. (Recall that $U(n)$ denotes the group of $n \times n$ complex unitary matrices.)

Let

$$V = v^\mu(x)\frac{\partial}{\partial x^\mu}$$

be a vector field on X. Let V_H be its horizontal lifting, i.e.,

$$V_H(z) = iA_\mu(x)V(z^\mu)z$$

$$= iA_\mu(x)v^\mu z$$

Thus,

$$V_H = v^\mu\frac{\partial}{\partial x^\mu} + iA_\mu(x)v^\mu z\frac{\partial}{\partial z} \quad .$$

Suppose $\gamma: X \to Y$ is a cross-section given by (14.1). We shall compute its *covariant derivative*, as defined in the last section. Note that

$$\psi = \gamma^*(z)$$

$$\gamma_t = \exp(tV_H)\gamma \exp(-tV)$$

$$\gamma_t^* = \exp(-tV)^*\gamma^* \exp(tV_H)^*$$

$$\frac{\partial}{\partial t}\gamma_t^*(z)\Big|_{t=0} = -V\gamma^*(z) + \gamma^* V_H(z)$$

$$= -V^\mu \frac{\partial}{\partial x^\mu}(\psi) + iA_\mu(x)V^\mu\psi$$

Thus, $\nabla_V\gamma$ is the cross-section determined by the map

$$V(\psi) - iA_\mu(x)V^\mu\psi$$

We can then write ("abus de langage")

$$\nabla_V\psi = V(\psi) - A(V)\psi \quad , \tag{14.1}$$

$$A = A_\mu dx^\mu \tag{14.2}$$

This shows how the electromagnetic potential one-form A operates as a *connection* (i.e., covariant derivative) on "Schrödinger wave functions" $x \to \psi(x)$.

For example, consider a "free" Schrödinger equation for a particle of mass m. Classically, the equation for "energy" is

$$E = \frac{1}{2m}\vec{p}^2$$

Quantum mechanically, this is

$$\left(i\frac{\partial}{\partial x^0} - \frac{1}{2m}\delta^{ij}\frac{\partial}{\partial x^i}\frac{\partial}{\partial x^j}\right)\psi = 0 \quad , \qquad 1 \le i,j \le 3$$

(Set Planck's constant equal to one.) Replace partial derivatives by covariant derivatives using (14.1).

$$0 = \left(i\left(\frac{\partial}{\partial x^0} - iA_0\right) - \frac{1}{2m}\delta^{ij}\left(\frac{\partial}{\partial x^i} - iA_i\right)\left(\frac{\partial}{\partial x^j} - iA_j\right)\right)\psi \tag{14.2}$$

Now, (14.2) is a differential equation for ψ, considered as a map: $X \to \mathbb{C}$. It also has great physical significance (as the equation for a charged particle moving in an electromagnetic field). We started off with Γ as the product vector bundle. But it might be a product in many ways. For example, we can write

$$\gamma_1(x) = (x, e^{i\lambda(x)} \psi_1(x)) ,$$

with ψ_1 alone a map: $X \to \mathbb{C}$, with $\lambda(x)$ a fixed real-valued function on X. (One wants "U(1)-isomorphisms", i.e., those preserving the structure group, not only for mathematical purposes, but also for physical reasons, e.g., to preserve the physical interpretation of $|\psi(x)|$ as a "probability".) One can now see that the differential operator (14.2) is the same when it is considered as acting on cross-sctions of the vector bundle, not the "Schrödinger wave functions" $x \to \psi(x)$. Thus, "quantum mechanics" should properly deal with *cross-sections of line bundles*, not with "complex-valued functions" This geometric interpretation is particularly emphasized in Kostant's and Souriau's work [9-11]. Note that physicists call this whole business "gauge invariance". It illustrates the fundamental observation that the "theory of gauge fields" is *identical* with the theory of fiber spaces!

15. ROTATIONALLY SYMMETRIC STATIONARY ELECTROMAGNETIC FIELDS

Simplifying all the "phenomenology", let us write Maxwell's equation as

$$\boxed{\begin{aligned} \frac{\partial B}{\partial t} &= -dE \\ \frac{\partial E}{\partial t} + J &= *d*B \\ dB &= 0 \\ d*E &= \rho dx \end{aligned}} \tag{15.1}$$

B, E, ρ are time-dependent one-forms on R^3. $*$ is the Hodge dual operation. ρ is a time-dependent function on R^3. $dx = dx^1 \wedge dx^2 \wedge dx^3$ is the Euclidean metric volume element. The pair (E,B) is the *electromagnetic field*. It is *stationary* if

$$\frac{\partial E}{\partial t} = 0 = \frac{\partial B}{\partial t} . \tag{15.2}$$

Equation (15.1) takes the form:

$$\begin{aligned} dE &= 0 = dB \\ \delta B &= J \\ d*E &= \rho dx . \qquad (\delta = *d*) . \end{aligned} \tag{15.3}$$

Let $\mathscr{G}$ be the Lie algebra of vector fields generated by the action of SO(3,R) on R^3. Thus, $\mathscr{G}$ has a basis V^i, with

$$V_i = \varepsilon_{ijk} x_j \frac{\partial}{\partial x_j} \quad . \tag{15.4}$$

Since we work with Euclidean geometry, there is no point to bothering with upper and lower indices. i,j,k run from 1 to 3. (x_i) are Euclidean coordinates, (ε_{ijk}) is completely skew-symmetric, and $\varepsilon_{123} = 1$. Denote $\partial/\partial x^i$ as ∂_i.

A differential form θ on R^3 is *rotationally symmetric* if

$$\mathscr{L}_{V^i}(\theta) = 0 \quad . \tag{15.5}$$

where $\mathscr{L}$ denotes Lie derivative.

Let us work out conditions (15.5) in case θ is a one-form. (This will determine the invariants for two-forms also, since they are isomorphic to one-forms under the Hodge dual operation

$$*dx_i = \varepsilon_{ijk}\, dx_j \wedge dx_k \quad .) \tag{15.6}$$

Suppose

$$\theta = a_i dx_i \tag{15.7}$$

$$0 = \mathscr{L}_{V_j}(\theta) = V_j(a_l)dx_i + a_i dV_j(x_i)$$

$$= V_j(a_i)dx_i + \varepsilon_{ijk} a_i dx_k$$

$$V_j(a_i) = -\varepsilon_{kji} a_k \quad . \tag{15.8}$$

Note that

$$V_j(x_i) = \varepsilon_{jk\ell} x_k \partial_\ell (x_i) = \varepsilon_{jki} x_k$$

$$= -\varepsilon_{kji} x_k$$

Note that the "a_i transform under $\mathscr{G}$ in the same way as the x_i".

<u>Exercise</u>. Show that the a_i must be of the form

$$a_i = f(r^2) x_i \quad , \tag{15.9}$$

where $r^2 = x_i x_i$. (Physicists call a general version of this the "Wigner-Eckert theorem". It is really a special case of the "Frobenius reciprocity theorem".

Thus we can look for E,B as solutions of (15.3) with E and B rotationally symmetric, i.e.,

$$E = f(r^2)x_i\,dx_i$$

$$B = g(r^2)x_i\varepsilon_{ijk}dx_j \wedge dx_k \tag{15.10}$$

$$= g(r^2)*(x_i dx_i) \quad .$$

Now,

$$x_i dx_i = \frac{1}{2}d(r^2) \quad .$$

Hence,

$$E = df \tag{15.11}$$

where f is a function of r^2. Similarly,

$$B = *dg$$

with g a function of r^2. Thus,

$$\rho\,dx = d{*E} = d{*df} \quad ,$$

$$\rho = *d{*df} = \Delta(f) \quad . \tag{15.12}$$

This is *Poisson's equation.*

We can work out the classical formula:

$$df = f'd(r^2) = 2f'x_i dx_i$$

$$\Delta(f) = 2\partial_i(f'x_i)$$

$$= 4f''x_ix_i + 6f'$$

$$= 4f''r^2 + 6f' \quad . \tag{15.13}$$

To define an "electric monopole" we can set (15.13) equal to zero, and set $r^2 = y$:

$$\frac{f''(y)}{f'(y)} = -\frac{3}{2}y^{-1}$$

$$\log f'(y) = -\frac{3}{2}\log y + x$$

$$f'(y) = cy^{-3/2}$$

$$f(y) = c_1 y^{-1/2} + c_2 \quad .$$

Because of its importance for Einstein's program, let us state this result formally.

Theorem 5.1. Any one-form θ on R^3 which is rotationally invariant is of the following form

$$\theta = df \quad ,$$

where f is a function of $r = (x_i x_i)^{1/2}$. If such a θ also satisfies

$$d{*}\theta = \rho\, dx \quad ,$$

where ρ is a function which is zero in an open subset of R^3, and then ρ is of the form

$$\theta = \lambda d(r^{-1}) \quad . \tag{15.14}$$

with λ a constant. In particular, if $E \in \mathscr{D}^1(R^3)$, $B \in \mathscr{D}^2(R^3)$ are spherically symmetric forms which satisfy the stationary form (15.3) of Maxwell's equation, with δ and ρ vanishing in some open subset of R^3, then

$$\begin{aligned} E &= \lambda_1 d(r^{-1}) \\ B &= \lambda_2 {*} d(r^{-1}) \end{aligned} \tag{15.15}$$

with constants λ_1, λ_2.

Ultimately, these "constants" (which essentially are the "charge of the electron" and "charge of the magnetic pole") should be "quantized" via some geometric and/or topological argument roughly parallel to that in Dirac's classical paper [2]. However, the physical literature surrounding this question is so muddled (relative to the meaning of the "global" nature of things) that it is not yet clear to me whether there is a "real" problem and/or phenomenon here. I will now pause in the mathematical development to discuss some points which the physicist might think are "trivial" (and they might well be!), but which I want to put down in order to clarify them in my own mind. Of course, the fact that the experiments have never found them should indicate that there might be some missing ingredient (particularly of "global differential geometry") that mathematical reasoning could clarify.

16. THE QUESTION OF "MAGNETIC POLES"

First, consider the *free* Maxwell equation which one obtains by setting $J = \rho = 0$ in (15.1)

$$\boxed{\begin{aligned} \frac{\partial B}{\partial t} &= -dE \\ \frac{\partial E}{\partial t} &= *d*B \\ dB &= 0 = d*E \end{aligned}} \tag{16.1}$$

E is a time-dependent one-form, B is a time-dependent two-form on R^3. $*$ is the Hodge-dual operation on differential forms specialized to the Euclidean metric on R^3. Note that

$$*(*\theta) = \theta \quad . \tag{16.2}$$

Suppose that (E,B) is a solution of (16.1). Set:

$$E' = *B \ ; \qquad B' = -*E \quad .$$

Then,

$$\frac{\partial E'}{\partial t} = * \frac{\partial B}{\partial t} = -*dE = *d*B'$$

$$\frac{\partial B'}{\partial t} = -* \frac{\partial E}{\partial t} = -*(*d*B)$$

$$= -d*B = -dE'$$

$$dB' = -d*E = 0$$

$$d*E' = d**B = dB = 0 \quad .$$

We conclude that

(E',B') *also satisfy the free Maxwell equations.*

This is like an "internal symmetry" in elementary particle physics; we may call it the *Dirac symmetry* of the free Maxwell equations. (It may, in fact, be already given some other name in the literature.)

Now, if one applies this Dirac symmetry to a pair (E,B) satisfying (15.1) with nonzero ϕ,J, we obtain a pair (E',B') satisfying a set of equations which we will now derive:

$$\frac{\partial E'}{\partial t} = * \frac{\partial B}{\partial t} = - *dE = *d*B'$$

$$\frac{\partial B'}{\partial t} = - * \frac{\partial E}{\partial t} = - *(*d*B - J)$$

$$= - d*B + *J$$

$$= - dE' + *J$$

$$dB' = - d*E = - \rho\, dx$$

$$d*E' = dB = 0 \quad .$$

Thus, (E',B') satisfy equations that we write in the following form:

$$\boxed{\begin{aligned} \frac{\partial E'}{\partial t} &= *d*B' \\ \frac{\partial B'}{\partial t} + J_m &= - dE' \\ dB' &= - \rho_m dx \\ dE' &= 0 \end{aligned}} \qquad (16.3)$$

ρ_m, J_m are the *magnetic charge current.*

In particular, we can get a solution of these equations by applying the Dirac-symmetry to the *electric monopole field,* i.e.,

$$\boxed{\begin{aligned} E &= \lambda d\left(\frac{1}{r}\right) \\ B &= 0 \end{aligned}} \qquad (16.4)$$

(λ is a constant.)

$$\boxed{\begin{aligned} B' &= \lambda * d\left(\frac{1}{r}\right) \\ E' &= 0 \end{aligned}} \qquad (16.5)$$

This field (B',E') is called the *field of the electric monopole.*

This meaning seems harmless enough. However, life gets interesting when we inquire about the *geometric* meaning of the electromagnetic field, e.g., in the Kaluza-Klein sense. This means that the geometric interpretation of the electromagnetic field

$$F = F_{\mu\nu} dx^{\mu} \wedge dx^{\nu}$$

as a two-form on R^4 *that is the Ehresmann curvature* of an Ehresmann connection on a line bundle is an essential ingredient.

A more traditional way of thinking of this is to consider "scalar and vector potentials". We now go into this.

17. SCALAR AND VECTOR POTENTIALS FOR STATIONARY ELECTROMAGNETIC FIELDS

First, consider the stationary Maxwell's equations with the currents and charges in the traditional place:

$$\boxed{\begin{aligned} dE &= 0 \\ *d*B &= J \\ dB &= 0 \\ *d*E &= \rho \end{aligned}} \qquad (17.1)$$

Equations (17.1) and the Poincaré lemma imply that (at least locally) there is a function ϕ and a one-form A such that

$$\begin{aligned} E &= d\phi \\ B &= dA \quad . \end{aligned} \qquad (17.2)$$

ϕ is the *scalar* (or electric) *potential*, A the vector (or *magnetic* potential).

Now, we consider the "Dirac symmetry"

$$\begin{aligned} E' &= *B \\ B' &= - *E \end{aligned} \qquad (17.3)$$

Then,

$$\begin{aligned} dE' &= *J = J' \\ dB' &= - *\rho = - \rho\, dx \equiv \rho'\, dx \quad . \end{aligned} \qquad (17.4)$$

Suppose that ρ',J' are zero outside of a closed subset S of R^3. (S is called the "singularity" or "source of magnetic poles" set.) Then, $R^3 - S$, we have

$$dB' = 0 = dE' \quad . \tag{17.5}$$

Thus ϕ',A' may exist locally in $R^3 - S$, but not necessarily globally. ("DeRham's theorem", i.e., the homology of $R^3 - S$ determines this.) On the other hand, these potentials are needed to set up a "Schrödinger equation".

Here is another way of looking at this. Consider a "particle" of mass m and charge e (technically, what is called a "test particle" in physics, i.e., it does not affect the electromagnetic field). Suppose its path is a curve $t \to x(t)$ in R^3. d^2x/dt^2 is its acceleration. Use the isomorphism between tangent spaces R^3_x and its dual to identify the acceleration vector with a tangent *covector*. Then, its equation is:

$$m \frac{d^2x}{dt^2} = e\left(E' + \frac{dx}{dt} \lrcorner B'\right) \quad . \tag{17.6}$$

We would like to "quantize" this equation; this seems to require (if we follow the usual procedure relating quantization to Hamilton-Jacobi theory) that potentials ϕ',A' exist *globally*. In fact, implicit in Dirac's argument [2] is a weaker condition, which was probably first isolated systematically by B. Kostant in connection with what he calls "geometric quantization". I will now develop this material from a certain point of view, then return to the study of the electromagnetic situation.

18. THE LINE BUNDLE DEFINED BY A CLOSED TWO-FORM ON A MANIFOLD

One key idea of connection theory to keep in mind is that a connection has an associated *curvature* tensor, which is a "two-differential form" on the base manifold of a more general type (i.e., it takes values in a vector bundle). Conversely, one may ask whether a given generalized two-form is the curvature form of *some* connection. In general, this is a difficult (and unsolved) problem. However, for certain types of connections, the curvature may be considered as a scalar-valued differential form, and the question may be completely answered. It appeared first in algebraic geometry, mainly in the work of A. Weil, K. Kodaira and D.C. Spencer in the 1950's, then later in Kostant's work in connection with "quantization". A full exposition is available in the book by Wallach [11] and I will refer the reader there for further details and references.

We will begin in a convenient way. Let

$$\pi: E \to X$$

be a vector bundle, with real vector spaces as fibers. $\Gamma(E)$ denotes the space of cross-sections, considered as an $\mathcal{F}(X)$-module. A *connection* for the vector bundle is an R-bilinear mapping

$$\nabla\colon \mathcal{V}(X) \times \Gamma(E) \to \Gamma(E) \quad ,$$

$$(V,\gamma) \to \nabla_V \gamma \quad ,$$

such that:

$$\nabla_{fV}\gamma = f\nabla_V\gamma$$

$$\nabla_V(f\gamma) = V(f)\gamma + f\nabla_V\gamma$$

$$\text{for } f \in \mathcal{F}(X) \ ; \quad V \in \mathcal{V}(X) \ ; \quad \gamma \in \Gamma(E) \quad .$$

For such a connection, its *curvature tensor* K is defined as follows

$$K(V_1,V_2)(\gamma) = \nabla_{V_1}\nabla_{V_2}(\gamma) - \nabla_{V_2}\nabla_{V_1}(\gamma) - \nabla_{[V_1,V_2]}\gamma \tag{18.1}$$

K is $\mathcal{F}(X)$-bilinear, i.e., it is a "tensor-field". Let E' be the vector bundle whose fiber above $x \in X$ is

$$L(E(x), E(x)) \quad ,$$

i.e., the space of linear maps: $E(X) \to E(X)$ of the fiber of E above x into itself. Then,

> K is a two-differential form on X with values in E' .

Thus, we have a "functorial" or "natural" mapping:

(vector bundles, connection) $\to$ two-forms on X of a certain type

As I said above, it would be desirable to have an effective way of characterizing the image of this mapping, i.e., a method of saying when a "tensor field" of a certain type is the curvature tensor of *some* vector bundle. Unfortunately, we do not have this information. However, here is a special case where we can do this, and which is extremely important for algebraic geometry, quantization, etc.

Suppose that each fiber of E is a one-dimensional, complex vector space, i.e., E is a (*complex*) *line bundle*. Then we can multiply each $\gamma \in \Gamma(E)$ with $i = \sqrt{-1}$, i.e., $\Gamma(E)$ becomes a complex vector space. $\mathcal{F}(X) \otimes \mathbb{C}$ ($\equiv$ the algebra of complex-valued C^∞ functions on X) acts on $\Gamma(E)$, i.e., $\Gamma(E)$ is an $\mathcal{F}(X)$-module.

Let us suppose that the connection ∇ satisfies the following condition:

$$\nabla_V(i\gamma) = i\nabla_V\gamma \tag{18.2}$$

for $v \in \mathscr{V}(X)$, $\gamma \in \Gamma(E)$

Another way of stating this is that ∇ is a connection relative to $\mathscr{F}(X) \otimes \mathbb{C}$, i.e.,

$$\nabla_X(f\gamma) = X(f)\gamma + f\nabla_X\gamma$$

for $f \in \mathscr{F}(X) \otimes \mathbb{C}$.

Then, using (18.1), we have:

$$K(V_1,V_2)(i\gamma) = iK(V_1,V_2)\gamma \tag{18.3}$$

Alternately, $K(V_1,V_2)$ is an $\mathscr{F}(X) \otimes \mathbb{C}$ linear map $\Gamma(E) \to \Gamma(E)$. Now, for $V_1,V_2 \in \mathscr{V}(X)$,

$$K(V_1,V_2) \text{ is an } \mathscr{F}(X)\text{-linear map } \Gamma(E) \to \Gamma(E) .$$

Since the fibers of E are one-dimensional complex vector spaces and $K(V_1,V_2)(x)$ is complex-linear, there is a complex-valued differential form

$$\omega\colon \mathscr{V}(X) \times \mathscr{V}(X) \to \mathscr{F}(X) \otimes \mathbb{C} \tag{18.4}$$

such that

$$K(V_1,V_2)(\gamma) = \omega(V_1,V_2)\gamma \tag{18.4}$$

for $V_1,V_2 \in \mathscr{V}(X)$

<u>Theorem 18.1</u>. ω is a closed two-form on X, i.e., $d\omega = 0$.

<u>Proof</u>. Since the result is "local", it suffices to prove it "locally", i.e., we can work on a sufficiently small open subset of X so that the vector bundle $\pi\colon E \to X$ is isomorphic to a product $X \times \mathbb{C}$. Alternately, this means that $\Gamma(E)$ has a basis γ_0 as an $\mathscr{F}(X) \otimes \mathbb{C}$-module. Let θ be the complex-valued one-form on X such that

$$\nabla_V\gamma_0 = \theta(V)\gamma_0$$

for $V \in \mathscr{V}(X)$.

Let V_1,V_2 be vector fields in X such that $[V_1,V_2] = 0$. Then,

$$\nabla_{V_1}\nabla_{V_2}\gamma_0 - \nabla_{V_2}\nabla_{V_1}\gamma_0 = K(V_1,V_2)(\gamma_0)$$

$$= \omega(V_1,V_2)(\gamma_0)$$

$$= \nabla_{V_1}(\theta(V_2)\gamma_0) - \nabla_{V_2}(\theta(V_1)\gamma_0)$$

$$= V_1(\theta(V_2))\gamma_0 + \theta(V_2)\theta(V_1)\gamma_0 - V_2(\theta(V_1))\gamma_0$$

$$- \theta(V_1)\theta(V_2)\gamma_0$$

Thus, we have:

$$\boxed{\omega = d\theta} \tag{18.5}$$

where $d\omega = 0$, by the $dd = 0$ property of exterior derivative.

Since this material is crucial for the Dirac-Kostant theory, let us summarize it. Let $\pi: E \to X$ be complex line bundle. ∇ can be defined as either an Ehresmann connection for (π,E,X) whose parallel transport is an isomorphism between the complex vector space structure of the fibers *or* as a linear covariant derivative operation satisfying (18.2).

Theorem 18.2. Suppose $\pi: E \to X$ is a complex line bundle over X and ∇^0,∇^1 are both connections for the bundle which satisfy (18.2). Let ω,ω' be the corresponding closed two-forms determined by the curvature of these connections. Then, ω and ω' belong to the same deRham cohomology class, i.e., there is a one-form η such that

$$\omega - \omega' = d\eta \quad . \tag{18.6}$$

Proof. Set:

$$\tau(X)(\gamma) = \nabla_X\gamma - \nabla'_X\gamma \tag{18.7}$$

i.e., τ is the "difference" of the vector bundle connections. Because of the cancellation of the non-tensorial term, τ is $\mathscr{F}(X)$-bilinear. It also satisfies

$$\tau(X)(i\gamma) = i\tau(X)\gamma$$

Hence, τ is determined by a one-form η in the following way:

$$\tau(X)(\gamma) = \eta(X)\gamma \quad .$$

(18.6) now readily follows.

Remark. These results are simple prototypes of a result for general connections developed in the general Chern-Weil transgression-characteristic class theory. The prototype for this was Chern's brilliant proof of the Gauss-Bonnet formula. See Spivak's "Comprehensive Introduction to Differential Geometry" [8] and Kobayashi-Nomizu [7].

19. QUANTIZATION BY MEANS OF COMPLEX LINEAR CONNECTIONS IN COMPLEX VECTOR BUNDLES

"Quantization" usually takes the following form. One is given a manifold X. Let $T^d(X)$ denote its cotangent bundle. Functions $f \in \mathscr{F}(T^d(X))$ admit the Poisson bracket operation. For a volume element form on X, put a Hilbert space structure on $\mathscr{F}(X) \otimes \mathbb{C}$

$$\langle\psi_1|\psi_2\rangle = \int_X \psi_1(x)^*\psi_2(x)\ dx$$

Try to assign Hermitian operators to elements $f \in \mathscr{F}(T^d(X))$ in such a way that Poisson bracket go onto operator commutator.

Now, part of $\mathscr{F}(T^d(X))$ can be realized *first* as first order, inhomogeneous differential operators on X. B. Kostant and J. Souriau added a new degree of freedom to the quantization question by remarking that it is useful to replace $\mathscr{F}(X) \otimes \mathbb{C}$ with the cross-sections $\Gamma(E)$ of a complex line bundle, with the representation of first order differential operators realized by a complex-linear connection in E. They found that in order to do so and assure that the resulting representation of the observables be by *Hermitian* operators in a *Hilbert* space, the curvature two-forms on X had to have integral *periods* on the cycles of X, i.e., its deRham cohomology class had to come from an element of $H^2(X,Z)$, the second degree cohomology classes of X with *integer* coefficients. In the usual physical problems, X is Euclidean space, so this condition is not interesting. However, for certain problems with more complicated topological conditions for the configuration space, this condition becomes very interesting indeed. In particular, for the Dirac momentum monopole

$$X = R^2 - (0) \quad ,$$

$$H^2(X,Z) = Z \quad .$$

(The generating two-cycle is just the unit sphere!) The Kostant-Souriau condition is identical with Dirac's, and provides for the "quantization". I believe this is very important as a prototype for more complicated nonlinear field theories, and might be the mechanism Einstein predicted--"quantum" effects for elementary particles obtained in a natural geometric way.

Let X be a manifold, and let

$$\pi: E \rightarrow X$$

be a complex vector bundle. $\Gamma(E)$, the space of cross-sections, is then an $\mathscr{F}(X) \otimes \mathbb{C}$-module.

Let ∇ be a Ehresmann connection whose parallel transport preserves the complex-linear structure in the fibers. As we have seen, it also determines a covariant derivative operator

$$\nabla: \mathscr{V}(X) \times \Gamma(E) \rightarrow \Gamma(E)$$

$$V, \gamma \rightarrow \nabla_V \gamma \quad .$$

$$\nabla_V(i\gamma) = i\nabla_V \gamma \quad .$$

Assign to each $f \in \mathscr{F}(X)$ the linear operator

$$h_f: \Gamma(E) \rightarrow \Gamma(E)$$

as follows:

$$h_f(\gamma) = f\gamma \quad . \tag{19.1}$$

Assign to each $v \in \mathscr{V}(X)$ the linear operator

$$h_V: \Gamma(E) \rightarrow \Gamma(E)$$

as follows:

$$h_V(\gamma) = i\nabla_V \gamma \tag{19.2}$$

Then,

$$h_V h_f(\gamma) = i\nabla_V(f\gamma)$$

$$= i\nabla_V(f)\gamma + if\nabla_V \gamma$$

$$h_f h_V(\gamma) = fi\nabla_V \gamma \quad .$$

Hence,

$$[h_V, h_f](\gamma) = i\nabla_V(f)\gamma \quad ,$$

i.e.,

$$[h_V, h_f] = i\nabla_V(f) \quad . \tag{19.3}$$

These are just a general version of the *Heisenberg commutation relations*, so that we are on the way to a "quantum mechanics". What we need for *physics* is a Hilbert space structure for $\Gamma(E)$ so that these operators h_f, h_V are *Hermitian*. This is provided (in Kostant's theory) by a geometric structure that differential geometers call a *Hermitian vector bundle*.

20. HERMITIAN VECTOR BUNDLES AND THEIR CONNECTIONS

Continue with the notation of Section 19. $\pi\colon E \to X$ is a complex vector bundle. For $x \in X$, the fiber $\pi^{-1}(x)$ is a complex vector space.

Suppose that, for each $x \in X$, this complex vector space $\pi^{-1}(x)$ has a Hermitian symmetric inner product

$$\langle \; | \; \rangle \quad .$$

This means that

$$(v_1, v_2) \to \langle v_1 | v_2 \rangle$$

is an R-linear mapping

$$\pi^{-1}(x) \times \pi^{-1}(x) \to \mathbb{C}$$

such that

$$\langle v | v \rangle > 0 \qquad \text{for} \quad v \in \pi^{-1}(x) - (0)$$

$$\langle v_1 | v_2 \rangle = \overline{\langle v_2 | v_1 \rangle}$$

(the overbar means complex conjugate, i.e., I use the mathematicians' notation. Physicists usually use *.)

$$\langle v_1 | iv_2 \rangle = i \langle v_1 | v_2 \rangle$$

$$\langle iv_1 | v_2 \rangle = -i \langle v_1 | v_2 \rangle \quad .$$

Further, suppose this inner product varies smoothly with x. The resulting geometric object is called a *Hermitian vector bundle*.

Definition. A linear connection ∇ for a Hermitian vector bundle is a connection (in the Ehresmann sense, or alternately, as covariant derivative) such that parallel transport over curves in the base is an isomorphism of the complex vector space and Hermitian inner product structure on the fibers. Such a connection can be characterized by the following conditions:

$$
\begin{aligned}
\nabla_V(i\gamma) &= i\nabla_V\gamma \\
V(\langle\gamma_1|\gamma_2\rangle) &= \langle\nabla_V\gamma_1|\alpha_2\rangle + \langle\gamma_1|\nabla_V\gamma_2\rangle \quad .
\end{aligned}
\tag{20.1}
$$

Suppose such a Hermitian connection is given. Let $\Gamma_0(E)$ denote the space of cross-sections $\gamma\colon X \to E$ which have *compact support*, i.e., which vanish outside of a compact subset of X. Let dx be a volume element form for X. Then, we can define an inner product on $\Gamma_0(E)$ which makes it a *pre-Hilbert space*

$$
(\gamma_1,\gamma_2) = \int_X \langle\gamma_1|\gamma_2\rangle \, dx \quad . \tag{20.2}
$$

(A "pre-Hilbert space" is a complex vector space with an inner product which satisfies all the "Hilbert space" axioms except *completeness*. In the physics literature, there is usually no distinction made.) For $V \in \mathscr{V}(X)$, let

$$\text{div}\ (V)$$

be the function such that

$$
\mathscr{L}_V(dx) = (\text{div}\ V)\,dx \quad . \tag{20.3}
$$

Set:

$$
h_V(\gamma) = i\nabla_V(\gamma) + \frac{i}{2}(\text{div}\ V)\gamma \quad . \tag{20.4}
$$

Theorem 20.1. h_V acting on $\Gamma_0(E)$ is--with respect to the inner product (20.2)--a symmetric ($\equiv$ "Hermitian", in physicists' language) operator.

Proof.

$$
\begin{aligned}
(\gamma_1,h_V\gamma_2) &= \int_X \langle\gamma_1|i\nabla_V\gamma_2 + \tfrac{1}{2}\,\text{div}\ V\ \gamma_2\rangle \, dx \\
&= \int_X (V(\langle\gamma_1|\gamma_2\rangle) - \langle\nabla_V\gamma_1|\gamma_2\rangle) \, dx + \frac{i}{2}\int_X \text{div}\ V \langle\gamma_1|\gamma_2\rangle \, dx
\end{aligned}
$$

$$= i \int_X \mathcal{L}_V(\langle\gamma_1|\gamma_2\rangle\, dx) - \langle\gamma_1|\gamma_2\rangle \mathcal{L}_V(dx) - \int_X \langle\nabla_V\gamma_1|\gamma_2\rangle\, dx$$

$$+ \frac{i}{2} \int_X (\text{div } V)\, \langle\gamma_1|\gamma_2\rangle\, dx$$

$$= i \int_X d(V \lrcorner (\langle\gamma_1|\gamma_2\rangle\, dx)) - \langle\gamma_1|\gamma_2\rangle (\text{div } V)\, dx$$

$$- \int_X \langle\nabla_V\gamma_1|\gamma_2\rangle\, dx + \frac{i}{2} \int (\text{div } V)\, \langle\gamma_1|\gamma_2\rangle\, dx \qquad (20.5)$$

Now, the first term on the right hand side vanishes, since, by Stokes' theorem, the integral can be converted to one over the boundary of X, while the integrand vanishes at sufficiently far away points of X (since γ_1, γ_2 have compact support). Thus, we are left with

$$(\gamma_1, h_V\gamma_2) = \int_X \langle i\nabla_V\gamma_1|\gamma_2\rangle\, dx + \int_X \langle (i/2)\text{div } V\, \gamma_1|\gamma_2\rangle\, dx$$

$$= (h_V\gamma_1, \gamma_2)$$

q.e.d.

Now, for $f \in \mathcal{F}(X)$, set

$$h_f\gamma = f\gamma \quad .$$

h_f is also a symmetric operator.

Theorem 20.2.

$$[h_V, h_f] = ih_{V(f)} \quad . \qquad (20.6)$$

The *proof* was given in Section 19. Thus, we have satisfied the generalized Heisenberg relations (20.6) on a pre-Hilbert space $\Gamma_0(E)$ by means of *symmetric* operators. Let $\mathcal{H}$ be the Hilbert space completion of $\Gamma_0(E)$. h_f is essentially *self-adjoint*, i.e., its closure in $\mathcal{H}$. is self-adjoint, i.e., is the infinitesimal generator of a one-parameter group of automorphisms of the Hilbert space structure. One can prove that h_V is essentially self-adjoint providing that V generates a *global* one parameter group of diffeomorphisms on X.

Thus, we see that (modulo certain technical details of functional analysis) we have defined a "quantization" procedure. That is as far as I want to go here. It suffices to say that there has been extensive work perfecting these ideas and that it has seemed to be a satisfactory set-up for realizing most of the physicist's ideas of quantum mechanics.

The new interesting feature of the Kostant-Souriau program for elementary particle physicists is that the *existence* of the Hermitian bundle imposes *topological* conditions. We now turn to this topic.

21. THE CURVATURE OF A HERMITIAN LINE BUNDLE BELONGS TO AN INTEGRAL COHOMOLOGY CLASS

Let $\pi: E \to X$ be a complex line bundle with a Hermitian structure on the fibers and a connection ∇ which preserves the Hermitian structure. The *curvature form* is then the two-differential form $\omega \in \mathcal{D}^2(X)$ such that

$$\nabla_{V_1}\nabla_{V_2}\gamma - \nabla_{V_2}\nabla_{V_1}\gamma - \nabla_{[V_1,V_2]}\gamma = i\omega(V_1,V_2)\gamma \qquad (21.1)$$

for $V_1,V_2 \in \mathcal{V}(X)$, $\gamma \in \Gamma(X)$

We know that

$$d\omega = 0 \quad .$$

Thus, ω determines a deRham cohomology class $\bar{\omega}$, which we denote as

$$\bar{\omega} \in H^2(X, \text{de Rham})$$

deRham cohomology (the cohomology defined by differential forms) comes with real coefficients automatically. There is a natural isomorphism with Čech cohomology with real coefficients

$$H^2(X, \text{deRham}) \approx H^2(X, \text{Čech}, R)$$

The inclusion $Z \to R$ defines a map

$$H^2(X, \text{Čech}, Z) \to H^2(X, \text{Čech}, R)$$

i.e., each Čech cocycle with integer coefficients determines one with real.

Theorem 21.1. A given $\omega \in \mathcal{D}^2(X)$ such that $d\omega = 0$ is the curvature class of a Hermitian connection on a Hermitian line bundle if and only if $1/2\pi$ times its image in $H^2(X, \text{Čech}, R)$ comes from an element of $H^2(X, \text{Čech}, Z)$.

Proof. Of course, I must assume that the reader knows sufficient topology to make sense of the jargon. See Warner [12] and Greenberg [13]. It should also be known to the reader that in computing Čech cohomology we can work with any covering of X by open subsets which are geodesically convex with respect to some Riemannian metric for X.

Suppose we start off with a Hermitian line bundle $\pi: E \to X$ and a Hermitian connection ∇. Choose a covering $\{U\} = \mathcal{U}$ such that the bundle is a product above each open subset U. Let $\Gamma_U(E)$ denote the cross-sections whose support lies on U. Let $\mathscr{F}_U(X)$ denote the functions on X whose support lies in U. Then, there is a $\gamma_U \in \Gamma(E)$ such that each $\Gamma_U(E)$ is of the form

$$\gamma = f\gamma_U \quad , \qquad f \in \mathscr{F}_U(X) \otimes \mathbb{C} \quad .$$

Then there is a real one-form θ_U such that

$$\nabla_U \gamma_U = i\theta_U(V)\gamma_U \tag{21.2}$$

$$\text{for each} \quad V \in \mathscr{V}(X) \quad .$$

θ_U determines ∇ in the open subset U. (It is, of course, this "local" identification of one-forms with line bundle connections which is the geometric mechanism for Kaluza-Klein.) Further, we can normalize the basis cross-section γ_U with respect to the Hermitian metric on the fibers so that

$$\langle\gamma_U|\gamma_U\rangle = 1 \quad . \tag{21.3}$$

Now, go on to consider what happens in the intersection

$$U \cap U'$$

of two open subsets U,U' of the covering $\mathcal{U}$. One basis γ_U can be expressed in terms of the other. In view of (21.2), this takes the following form:

$$\gamma_U = e^{if_{UU'}} \gamma_{U'} \tag{21.4}$$

where $f_{UU'} \in \mathscr{F}(U \cap U')$. In the intersection $U \cap U' \cap U''$ of three open subsets of the covering, we have

$$\gamma_U = e^{if_{UU'}} \gamma_{U'} = e^{if_{UU'}} e^{if_{U'U''}} \gamma_{U''}$$

$$= e^{if_{UU''}} \gamma_{U''} \quad ,$$

i.e.,

$$\begin{aligned} f_{UU''} = f_{UU'} - f_{U'U''} &= 2\pi \times (\text{integer}) \\ &= 2\pi\eta_{UU'U''} \quad . \end{aligned} \tag{21.5}$$

Now, consider the one-form θ_U which locally determines the connection. We know that

$$d\theta_U = \omega \equiv \text{curvature two-form} \quad . \tag{21.6}$$

In $U \cap U'$,

$$\begin{aligned} \nabla_V \gamma_U &= i\theta_U(V)\gamma_U \\ &= \nabla_V\left(e^{if_{UU'}} \gamma_{U'}\right) \\ &= \gamma_U iV(f_{UU'}) + e^{if_{UU'}} i\theta_{U'}(V)\gamma_{U'} \\ &= \gamma_U iV(f_{UU'}) + \gamma_U i\theta_{U'}(V) \quad , \end{aligned}$$

i.e.,

$$\theta_U - \theta_{U'} = df_{UU'} \quad . \tag{21.7}$$

Now, the $\{\eta_{UU'U''}\}$ obtained from (21.5) defines an *integer* coefficient Čech cochain. Putting these formulas together with the way the isomorphism between Čech and deRham cohomology is defined, we see that the cohomology class $\bar{\omega}$ determines is precisely that determined by $\{\eta_{UU'U''}\}$. This proves Theorem 21.1 one way; the converse is readily obtained by reversing the reasoning.

This result is beautifully simple, once one understands the machinery, but is amazingly powerful for "quantization" purposes. In the next section we will see that it gives precisely Dirac's quantization condition for the magnetic monopole! Even more interesting, is the possibility of seeking generalizations for *nonlinear* Yang-Mills theories, i.e., Hermitian connections for higher dimensional Hermitian vector bundles.

To say that the curvature of the connection belongs to an integral Čech cohomology class is not an optimally useful statement, since Čech cohomology is not readily computable. However, Čech cohomology is isomorphic to *singular* cohomology based in differentiable simplices. Thus, we can rephrase the condition by saying that:

ω, the curvature, has integral periods over the differentiable two-cycles of X.

In certain cases, $H^2(X,Z)$ is generated by two-dimensional compact submanifolds of X. In this case, the condition can be written in "integral-geometric" form

$$\boxed{\int_S \omega = 2\pi \times (\text{integer})} \tag{21.8}$$

where S runs through the two-dimensional compact orientable submanifolds of X.

I do not want to go further into the technicalities of algebraic topology at the moment. Instead, let us turn to Dirac's example where the topological condition gives Dirac's "quantization" condition in a very beautiful way.

22. THE COMPLEX LINE BUNDLE DETERMINED BY THE DIRAC MAGNETIC MONOPOLE AND ITS CURVATURE

Now, specialize the material in Section 21 as follows:

$$X = R^3 - (0)$$

$$\omega = \lambda * d\left(\frac{1}{r}\right) \tag{22.1}$$

λ is a constant. r is the distance function $|x|$ on R^3. $*$ is the Hodge dual operation on R^3 with respect to the Euclidean metric. In order to tell whether the cohomology class determined by ω is an integer class, it suffices (we can prove) to apply (21.8); in fact, the only compact submanifold that matters is the two-sphere

$$S = \{x \in R^3 : |x| = 1\} \quad .$$

The integral

$$\int_S \omega \tag{22.2}$$

is then something like the "residue" of ω ($\equiv$ the magnetic field of the magnetic monopole) at its "singularity", $r = 0$. We will compute the integral (22.2) using standard integral-geometric techniques.

$$S = \{x \in R^3 : |x| = r_0\} \quad .$$

S is a submanifold of R^3. Set:

$$A = \text{grad}\,(r) = \frac{\partial r}{\partial x_i}\frac{\partial}{\partial x_i} = \frac{1}{r}x_i\frac{\partial}{\partial x_i} \quad ,$$

$$\langle A, A \rangle = 1 \quad .$$

($\langle\,,\,\rangle$ denotes the inner product on tangent vector fields and differential forms defined by the Euclidean metric

$$ds^2 = dx_i dx_j \quad ,$$

on R^3, $1 \le i,j \le 3$.) Thus, $A \lrcorner dx$ is the area of S, i.e.,

$$\int_S (A \lrcorner dx) = \text{area of } S \tag{22.2}$$

$$= 4\pi r_0^2 \quad .$$

Now,

$$\left\langle *d\left(\frac{1}{r}\right), A \lrcorner dx \right\rangle = \left\langle dr, *d\left(\frac{1}{r}\right), dx \right\rangle$$

$$= \left\langle dr, d\left(\frac{1}{r}\right)\right\rangle \langle dx, dx \rangle$$

$$= \left\langle dr, d\left(\frac{1}{r}\right)\right\rangle$$

$$= -\frac{1}{r^2}$$

Hence,

$$\int_S \omega = -\lambda 4\pi \tag{22.3}$$

$$\boxed{\lambda = \frac{\text{integer}}{4\pi}}$$

is the condition that ω define a cohomology class in $R^3 - (0)$. This is also the Dirac "monopole" quantization condition! I consider this argument one of the most beautiful I have ever seen in mathematical physics, a convincing argument for the permanent value of the Kostant-Souriau line-bundle modification of the idea of "quantization" (I was always a bit skeptical!) and a very suggestive source of new ideas about the way to realize "quantum" ideas in a way that is compatible with "geometry". Thus, I see this argument as a major clue to what an Einstein theory of elementary particles would be.

Of course, a natural question to ask is how the complex line bundles predicted by Dirac's monopole are actually constructed. This can be done in a purely group-theoretic way.

23. GROUP-THEORETIC CONSTRUCTION OF THE COMPLEX LINE-BUNDLES ON $R^3 - (0)$ CORRESPONDING TO THE DIRAC MAGNETIC MONOPOLE

Continue with X as $R^3 - (0)$. Let G be the rotation group $SO(3,R)$. It acts on X in the usual way. Its orbits are concentric spheres about the origin of radius r.

Let R^+ be the positive real numbers considered as a Lie group via multiplication. Let R^+ act on R^3 as "dilations", $\rho \in R^+$ acting on $x \in R^3-(0)$ is

$$\rho x \quad .$$

The direct product group

$$R^+ \times G$$

then acts *transitively* on X

$$(\rho,g)(x) = \rho g(x) = g(\rho x) \quad ,$$

(i.e., R^+ and G commute when acting on X, hence their product acts).

The isotropy subgroup of $R^+ \times G$ at a point $x \in X$ is obviously isomorphic to an $SO(2,R)$-subgroup of G, i.e.,

> X is the base space of a principal bundle
> with structure group $SO(2,R)$.

Exercise. Show that the complex line bundles defined by Dirac's magnetic monopole are those defined by taking a unitary representation

$$\sigma: SO(2,R) \to L(\mathbb{C})$$

and constructing the associated vector bundle. Investigate whether the connection whose curvature is ω is associated with the Ehresmann connection for the coset space

$$G \times R^+(SO(2,R)) \quad .$$

(If L is a connected Lie group, K a compact subgroup, the principal bundle $L \to L/K$ has an Ehresmann connection obtained by writing $\mathscr{L}$, the Lie algebra of L, as a direct sum $\mathscr{L} \equiv K \oplus \mathscr{M}$,

$$\text{Ad}\, K(\mathscr{M}) = \mathscr{M} \quad .$$

This decomposition can be made because finite dimensional representations of compact Lie groups are completely reducible.)

24. CONFORMAL COVARIANCE OF MAXWELL'S EQUATIONS

In the last section we have exploited group invariance properties of Maxwell's equations in a very simple way. Now the largest group of symmetries is the conformal group. (The most interesting proof of this is by the technique developed by Estabrook and Harrison [14].) Hence, ultimately we should attempt a classification of the line bundle associated with Maxwell's equations in terms of the conformal group. (Of course, there is also the relation between "Maxwell's equations" and "conformal *connections*" that is explicit in Herman Weyl's "Unified Field Theory". I intend to get to this later on.) First, I will develop the relations between the Hodge $\star$-operator and conformal transformations and for general Riemannian manifolds.

Let X be an n-dimensional manifold with a Riemannian metric $\langle\,,\rangle$, considered as an inner product on differential forms. A diffeomorphism

$$\phi: X \to X$$

is *conformal* if there is an $f \in \mathscr{F}(X)$ such that

$$\langle\phi^*(\theta),\, \phi^*(\theta')\rangle = f^2\phi^* \langle\theta,\theta'\rangle \tag{24.1}$$

for $\theta,\theta' \in \mathscr{D}^1(X)$.

Note that:

$$\langle\phi^*(\theta),\, \phi^*(\theta')\rangle = f^{2m,\phi^2}(\langle\theta,\theta'\rangle) \tag{24.2}$$

for $\theta,\theta' \in \mathscr{D}^m(X)$.

Example. Proof of (24.2) for $m = 2$. Suppose

$$\theta = \omega_1 \wedge \omega_2\,, \qquad \theta' = \omega_1' \wedge \omega_2'$$

$$\omega_1,\omega_2,\omega_1',\omega_2' \in \mathscr{D}^1(X) \quad .$$

$$\begin{aligned}\langle\phi^*(\theta),\phi^*(\theta')\rangle &= \langle\phi^*(\omega_1)\wedge\phi^*(\omega_2),\, \phi^*(\omega_1')\wedge\phi^*(\omega_2')\rangle \\ &= \langle\phi^*(\omega_1),\phi^*(\omega_1')\rangle\langle\phi^*(\omega_2),\phi^*(\omega_2')\rangle - \langle\phi^*(\omega_1),\phi^*(\omega_2')\rangle\langle\phi^*(\omega_2),\phi^*(\omega_1')\rangle \\ &= f^4\phi^*(\langle\theta,\theta'\rangle)\end{aligned}$$

q.e.d.

Let dx be the Riemannian volume element differential form, i.e.,

$$dx \in \mathscr{D}^n(X)$$

$$\langle dx, dx \rangle = 1$$

Thus,

$$1 = \phi^* \langle dx, dx \rangle = f^{-2n} \langle \phi^*(dx), \phi^*(dx) \rangle$$

hence,

$$\phi^*(dx) = f^n dx \quad .$$

The Hodge $*$ operator is characterized by the following identity:

$$\theta \wedge *\theta' = \langle \theta, \theta' \rangle \, dx$$

$$\text{for} \quad \theta, \theta' \in \mathscr{D}^m(X)$$

Thus,

$$\begin{aligned} \phi^*(\theta) \wedge \phi^*(*\theta') &= \phi^*(\langle \theta, \theta' \rangle) \phi^*(dx) \\ &= f^{-2m} \langle \phi^*(\theta), \phi^*(\theta') \rangle f^n dx \\ &= f^{n-2m} \phi^*(\theta) \wedge *\phi^*(\theta') \quad , \end{aligned}$$

i.e.,

$$\boxed{\begin{aligned} &f^{n-2m} * \phi^*(\theta) = \phi^*(*\theta') \\ &\text{for} \quad \theta \in \mathscr{D}^r(X) \end{aligned}} \tag{24.3}$$

This is the basic identity which determines the "conformal" properties of differential equations (e.g., Maxwell's) describable by Hodge's methods. (See Interdisciplinary Mathematics, Volume 4.) For example,

$$n = 4, \quad r = 2$$

$$\phi^*(*\theta) = *\phi^*(\theta) \quad .$$

This gives conformal *invariance* of the Maxwell equations. $\theta \in \mathscr{D}^2(R^4)$ satisfies *Maxwell* if $d\theta = 0$, $*d*\theta = J$. Then,

$$d\,\phi^*(\theta) = 0 \ ; \qquad *d*(\phi^*(\theta)) = \phi^*(J) \quad .$$

Let us now look at the conformal properties of the Dirac monopole field in $R^3 - (0)$

$$\theta = *d\left(\frac{1}{r}\right) = -\frac{1}{r^2} *dr \in \mathcal{D}^2(R^3) \quad .$$

Suppose

$$\phi^*(r) = \frac{1}{r} \quad ,$$

i.e., ϕ is the "inversion" operation. Then

$$\phi^*(dr) = -\frac{1}{r^2} dr \quad .$$

$$\langle dr, dr \rangle = \left\langle \frac{x_i dx_i}{r}, \frac{x_i dx_i}{r} \right\rangle$$

$$= 1$$

Hence,

$$\phi^*(\langle dx, dr \rangle) = 1 = f^2 \langle \phi^*(dr), \phi^*(dr) \rangle$$

$$= f^2 r^{-4} \langle dr, dr \rangle \quad ,$$

i.e.,

$$\boxed{f = r^2}$$

Then, using (24.1),

$$\phi^*\left(*d\left(\frac{1}{r}\right)\right) = f^{3-2} * \phi^*\left(d\left(\frac{1}{r}\right)\right)$$

$$= r^2 * \phi^*\left(d\left(\frac{1}{r}\right)\right)$$

$$= r^2 * d\phi^*\left(\frac{1}{r}\right)$$

$$= r^2 * dr = -r^4 * d\left(\frac{1}{r}\right) \quad .$$

Then,

$$\boxed{\phi^*(B) = -r^4 B} \tag{24.4}$$

where $B \in \mathcal{D}^2(R^3-(0))$ is the magnetic field of the Dirac magnetic monopole.

Bibliography

1. T.T. Wu and C.N. Yang, Phys. Rev. D 12 (1975), 3145.

2. P.A.M. Dirac, Proc. Roy. Soc. A 133 (1931), 60.

3. J.D. Jackson, Classical Electrodynamics, Wiley, N.Y., 1962.

4. G. deRham, Varietés Différentiables, Hermann, Paris, 1955.

5. W.V.D. Hodge, Harmonic Integrals, Cambridge University Press, Cambridge, England, 1940.

6. N. Steenrod, Topology of Fiber Bundles, Princeton University Press, Princeton, N.J., 1950.

7. S. Kobayashi and K. Nomizu, Foundations of Differential Geometry, Wiley, N.Y., 1964.

8. M. Spivak, A Comprehensive Introduction to Differential Geometry, Publish or Perish Press, Berkeley, CA.

9. B. Kostant, Quantization and Unitary Representations, Lecture Notes in Math, Vol. 170, 87-208, Springer-Verlag, Berlin.

10. J. Souriau, Structure des Systèmes Dynamique, Dinod, Paris, 1970.

11. N. Wallach, Symplectic Geometry and Fourier Analysis, Math Sci Press, Brookline, Mass., 1977.

12. F. Warner, Foundations of Differential Geometry and Lie Groups, Scott Foresman, Glenview, N.Y., 1973.

13. M. Greenberg, Lectures in Algebraic Topology, W. Benjamin, 1968.

14. F. Estabrook and B.W. Harrison, "Geometric Approach to Invariance Groups and Solutions of Partial Differential Equations", J. Math. Phys. 12 (1971), 653-666.

Chapter III

THE DIFFERENTIAL-GEOMETRIC THEORY OF QUANTUM MECHANICS "LOCAL" AND "GLOBAL" QUANTIZATION

1. INTRODUCTION

What I am calling the *Einstein program* for elementary particle physics involves integrating quantum mechanics into the *geometric* description of physics that was seen in Einstein's work. Of course, quantum mechanics *itself* has a geometric foundation, so that is the obvious place to begin. In the previous chapter we found that the Kostant-Souriau Hermitian line-bundle quantization was ideally suited to the description of the "quantization" of the Dirac magnetic monopole. This is a powerful argument in its favor, and I now want to develop certain general ideas that might be useful in further work.

An obvious generalization involves consideration of *complex vector bundles* with fibers of arbitrary dimension. Physically this is reminiscent of "Yang-Mills" replacing "Maxwell". In this case the "functor" (linear differential operator) → (symbol) which maps differential operators into cross-sections of bundles becomes more complicated and its application to quantum mechanics requires major new mathematical developments. An obvious first question to ask is: When does the space of "symbols" admit a Poisson bracket-like operation? The question will be analyzed here in a very preliminary way. Then, I will go on to further work concerning a general geometric setting for Dirac's "monopole" idea.

2. QUANTUM MECHANICS AS THE STUDY OF HERMITIAN LINEAR DIFFERENTIAL OPERATORS IN HERMITIAN VECTOR BUNDLES AND THEIR SYMBOLS

My basic point of view is that expressed in the long-winded title to this section. Thus, it sees *quantum mechanics* first as given, then as determining *classical mechanics*. The mathematical parallel to this is the "functor"

(linear differential operators in vector bundles)
→ (their "symbols" as cross-sections of certain vector bundles)

Dirac said:

> "Quantum mechanics means Poisson bracket goes into operator commutator."

From the point of view of contemporary differential geometry, it is the reverse--the operation that the "symbols" of linear differential operators inherit from operator commutator is Poisson bracket.

We can now be more explicit. Let

$$\pi: E \to X$$

be a complex vector bundle over a manifold X. Suppose X is real (i.e., do not assume that it has the structure of complex-analytic manifold). Let $\mathscr{F}(X) \otimes \mathbb{C}$ denote the algebra of C^∞, complex-valued functions on X, and let $\Gamma(E)$ be the space of cross-sections of the bundle. Let $\Gamma_0(E)$ be the subset of $\Gamma(E)$ consisting of the *compact support* cross-sections. Let $\mathscr{F}_0(X) \times \mathbb{C}$ denote the complex-valued, compactly supported C^∞ functions on X. We shall consider $\Gamma(E)$ as a $\mathscr{F}(X) \otimes \mathbb{C}$-module.

In [18] I have defined a general algebraic notion of "linear differential operator" to cover this concept. Let $D^m(\Gamma(E))$ be the m-th order ($\mathbb{C}$-linear) differential operators. I will now describe this in local terms. Let (x^i), $1 \leq i,j \leq n$, be a coordinate system for X. (Summation convention!) Set

$$\partial_i = \frac{\partial}{\partial x^i}, \qquad \partial_{ij} = \frac{\partial^2}{\partial x^i \partial x^j},$$

$$\partial_{i_1 \cdots i_m} = \frac{\partial^m}{\partial x^{i_1} \cdots \partial x^{i_m}}$$

Let us suppose that γ^a, $1 \leq a,b \leq m$, is a basis for $\Gamma(E)$ as an $\mathscr{F}(X) \otimes \mathbb{C}$-module. Thus, a $\gamma \in \Gamma(E)$ can be written as follows

$$\gamma = \psi_a \gamma^a \quad . \tag{2.1}$$

The ψ_a are objects the physicists would use to describe quantum mechanical situations. A $\Delta \in D^m(\Gamma(E))$ then takes the following form:

$$\Delta(\gamma) = \left(A_a^{i_1 \cdots i_m, b} \partial_{i_1 \cdots i_m}(\psi_b) + \cdots \right) \gamma^a \tag{2.2}$$

The terms $\cdots$ denote terms of lower order in the derivatives. The coefficients $A_{(\ )}^{(\ )}$ are complex-valued, C^∞ functions on X.

Let $T^d(X)$ denote the cotangent bundle to X. A point of $T^d(X)$ then consists of a point (x,θ) with $x \in X$, θ a linear map $X_x \to R$. Define a vector bundle

$$\pi': E'' \to T^d(X)$$

as follows:

A point of E' is a pair (x,θ,α), where $x \in X$, $\theta \in X_x^d$, α as a $\mathbb{C}$-linear map $\pi^{-1}(x) \to \pi^{-1}(x)$.

Let $p_i \in \mathscr{F}(T^d(X))$ be the functions defined as

$$p_i(x,\theta) = \theta(\partial_i) \quad . \tag{2.4}$$

(Physically, the p_i are the "momenta" conjugate to the variables x^i.)

<u>Definition</u>. The *symbol* of the differential operator $\Delta \in D^m(\Gamma(E))$ is the cross-section map $\sigma(\Delta): T^d(X) \to E'$ defined as follows:

$$\sigma(\Delta)(x,\theta)(\gamma^b(x)) = A_a^{i_1 \ldots i_m, b}(x)\, p_{i_1 \ldots i_m}(\theta)\gamma^a(x) \tag{2.5}$$

One can prove--using the purely algebraic machinery given in [15,18]--that $\sigma(\Delta)$ as defined by (2.5) is actually independent of the choices made for coordinates and a basis of cross-sections. Note that

$$\sigma(\Delta) = 0 \quad \text{if and only if} \quad \Delta \in D^{m-1}(\Gamma(E)) \quad . \tag{2.6}$$

Having defined the basic functor

$$\Delta \to \sigma(\Delta)$$

that is the mathematical analogue of the physicists' "correspondence principle"

(quantum mechanics) $\to$ (classical mechanics) ,

let us turn to imposing Hermitian conditions. This will provide a mechanism for introducing "probabilities".

The vector bundle $\pi: E \to X$ (whose fibers are finite dimensional complex vector spaces) is a *Hermitian vector bundle* if, for each $x \in X$, the fiber

$$E(x) = \pi^{-1}(x)$$

has a Hermitian positive-definite inner product $<|>$. As x varies, this defines an inner product

$$<\gamma_1|\gamma_2>(x) = <\gamma_1(x)|\gamma_2(x)>$$

on cross-sections. This inner product has the following properties:

$<|>$ is an $\mathscr{F}(X)$-bilinear map $\Gamma(E) \times \Gamma(E) \to \mathscr{F}(X) \otimes \mathbb{C}$.

$<\gamma|\gamma> \geq 0$

$<\gamma|\gamma> \equiv 0$ if and only if $\gamma(x) = 0$ for all x

$<\gamma_1|i\gamma_2> = i<\gamma_1|\gamma_2> = -<i\gamma_1|\gamma_2>$

$$\overline{\langle\gamma_1|\gamma_2\rangle} = \langle\gamma_2|\gamma_1\rangle$$

(Following the usage in the mathematical literature, complex conjugation is denoted by a bar. The asterisk is used in physics. We will present a special notation below for "Hermitian conjugate" of operators, so as not to conflict with asterisks as the pull-back map on functions.)

Suppose X is orientable, and fix dx as a volume element form for X. Define a $\mathbb{C}$-valued inner product on $\Gamma_0(E)$ as follows

$$(\gamma_1,\gamma_2) = \int_X \langle\gamma_1|\gamma_2\rangle \; dx \tag{2.7}$$

This inner product defines $\Gamma_0(E)$ as a *pre-Hilbert space*. Let $\mathscr{H}(E)$ denote its completion. This Hilbert space is the playground for geometric quantum mechanics!

A linear *differential* operator is now a linear map

$$\Delta: \Gamma_0(E) \to \Gamma_0(E) \quad .$$

Its *Hermitian adjoint*, denoted as $h(\Delta)$ is the linear differential operator $:\Gamma_0(E) \to \Gamma_0(E)$ such that

$$(\Delta\gamma_1,\gamma_2) = (\gamma_1,h(\Delta)\gamma_2) \tag{2.8}$$

for $\gamma_1,\gamma_2 \in \Gamma_0(E) \quad .$

We can now extend this Hermitian adjoint operator to certain more general sorts of linear maps (e.g., certain integral operators). The inner product (2.7) obviously makes sense where $\gamma_1 \in \Gamma(E)$. Suppose

$$\alpha: \Gamma_0(E) \to \Gamma(E)$$

is a linear map. The linear map

$$h(\alpha): \Gamma_0(E) \to \Gamma(E)$$

is said to be its *Hermitian adjoint* if

$$(\alpha\gamma_1,\gamma_2) = (\gamma_1,h(\alpha)\gamma_2)$$

for $\gamma_1,\gamma_2 \in \Gamma_0(E)$

For us, "quantum mechanics" will mean the study of Hermitian vector bundles, linear Hermitian operators, and their commutators. We will begin with simple examples.

3. FIRST ORDER LINEAR DIFFERENTIAL OPERATORS AND THEIR COMMUTATORS

Let us now work locally, so that E is the product

$$X \times V \quad ,$$

where V is a complex vector space with a positive definite Hermitian inner product $\langle | \rangle$. $\Gamma(E)$ will be identified with the space of linear maps

$$\psi: X \to V \quad ,$$

that we denote as $\mathcal{M}(X,V)$. (Physicists might call them "Schrödinger wave functions." In general, it is useful for "global" purposes to keep the distinction between $\mathcal{M}(X,V)$ and $\Gamma(E)$.)

Consider two first order linear differential operators: $\mathcal{M}(X,V) \to \mathcal{M}(X,V)$

$$\begin{aligned} \alpha &= \alpha^i \partial_i \\ \beta &= \beta^i \partial_i \quad . \end{aligned} \tag{3.1}$$

α_i, β_i are x-dependent linear maps: $V \to V$. Precisely, if $L(V)$ denotes the space of linear maps, $V \to V$, they are maps $X \to L(V)$, i.e., elements of $\mathcal{M}(X,L(V))$. Then

$$\begin{aligned} [\alpha,\beta](\psi) &= \alpha^i \partial_i \beta^j \partial_j(\psi) - \beta^j \partial_j \alpha^i \partial_i(\psi) \\ &= \alpha^i \partial_i(\beta^j)\partial_j(\psi) + \alpha^i \beta^j \partial_i \partial_j(\psi) - \beta^j \partial_j(\alpha^i)\partial_i(\psi) \\ &\quad - \beta^j \alpha^i \partial_j \partial_i(\psi) \end{aligned}$$

Hence

$$\boxed{[\alpha,\beta] = (\alpha^i \partial_i(\beta^j) - \beta^i \partial_i(\alpha^j))\partial_j + [\alpha^i,\beta^j]\partial_i\partial_j} \tag{3.2}$$

Now, in the scalar-valued case, i.e., $V = \mathbb{C}$, the second term on the right hand side of (3.2) vanishes. This leads to the basic differential geometric notion of *Jacobi bracket.*

The *symbol* of these operators is given as follows

$$\begin{aligned} \sigma(\alpha) &= \alpha^i p_i \\ \sigma(\beta) &= \beta^j p_j \quad . \end{aligned} \tag{3.3}$$

Again, in the scalar-valued case, we have:

$$\sigma([\alpha,\beta]) = \{\sigma(\alpha),\sigma(\beta)\} \quad , \tag{3.4}$$

where $\{\ ,\ \}$ denotes the classic Poisson bracket. This relation is the genesis of the whole spectrum of relations between differential geometry and quantum mechanics.

Now, a basic difference in the scalar-valued case (i.e., $V = \mathbb{C}$) and the more general one is that the commutator of first order differential operators may be a *second* order operator. This suggests that it might be useful to consider modifications of the Poisson bracket in order to restore the relation (3.4). Since it is the *commutator* of two linear maps which is involved, it appears to me that the basic geometric operation is a *Poisson-bracket-like* operator for Lie algebra-valued functions on a symplectic manifold. Although I am not prepared to give a definitive discussion, I will now present several partial results which will put us on that route.

4. A GENERALIZATION OF THE CLASSICAL POISSON BRACKET

Work with R^{2n} with coordinates (x^i,p_i), $1 \leq i,j \leq n$. Let $\mathscr{A}$ be a finite dimensional *associative* algebra over the real numbers as field of scalars. (For certain purposes, e.g., quantum field theory, it will be of interest to allow $\mathscr{A}$ to be infinite dimensional. Since this involves additional functional analysis difficulties--although no real conceptual problems from the point of view of differential geometry--I will not worry about it here.) Let $\mathscr{M}(R^{2n},\mathscr{A})$ be the space of C^∞ maps $R^{2n} \to \mathscr{A}$.

Remark. $\mathscr{M}(R^{2n},\mathscr{A})$ can also be considered as the tensor product

$$\mathscr{A} \otimes \mathscr{F}(R^{2n}) \quad .$$

Set

$$\partial_j = \frac{\partial}{\partial x^i} \quad ; \quad \partial^i = \frac{\partial}{\partial p^i} \quad .$$

Denote elements of $\mathscr{M}(R^{2n},\mathscr{A})$ as $\underline{A}$. Set:

$$\{\underline{A}_1,\underline{A}_2\} = \partial^i(\underline{A}_1)\partial_i(\underline{A}_2) - \partial^i(\underline{A}_2)\partial_i(\underline{A}_1) + [\underline{A}_1,\underline{A}_2] \tag{4.1}$$

In (4.1) $[\ ,\ ]$ denotes the Lie algebra on $\mathscr{A}$ obtained as the commutator of its associated algebra structure, i.e.,

$$[A_1,A_2] = A_1A_2 - A_2A_1$$

for $A_1,A_2 \in \mathscr{A}$.

Notice that (4.1) reduces to the usual Poisson bracket in case $\mathscr{A} = R$. It is often useful to think of (4.1) from the point of view of tensor product isomorphism

$$\mathscr{M}(R^{2n},\mathscr{A}) \approx \mathscr{A} \otimes \mathscr{F}(R^{2n}) .$$

$$\{A_1 \otimes f_1, A_2 \otimes f_2\} = A_1A_2 \otimes \partial^i(f_1)\partial_i(f_2) - A_2A_1 \otimes \partial^i(f_2)\partial_i(f_1) + [A_1,A_2] \otimes f_1f_2 \tag{4.2}$$

The third term on the right hand side of (4.2) is the "gauge Lie algebra" construction, while the first two terms are analogues of "Schwinger terms". See my books, Lie Algebras and Quantum Mechanics, "Interdisciplinary Mathematics", Volume 6, and [12]. Unfortunately, the Jacobi identity is not satisfied for this operation, i.e., it does not define a Lie algebra structure on $\mathscr{M}(R^{2n},\mathscr{A})$ *unless special conditions are imposed.* In fact, these "special conditions" might be important physically!

Of course, one can define the Poisson bracket between elements of $\mathscr{F}(R^{2n})$ and $\mathscr{M}(R^{2n},\mathscr{A})$:

$$\{f,\underline{A}\} = f^i\underline{A}_i - \underline{A}^i f_i \tag{4.3}$$

for $f \in \mathscr{F}(R^{2n})$, $\underline{A} \in \mathscr{M}(R^{2n},\mathscr{A})$.

Note that the usual proof of the Jacobi identity does generalize in the following "weak" form:

$$\{f_1,\{f_2,\underline{A}\}\} = \{\{f_1,f_2\},\underline{A}\} + \{f_2,\{f_1,\underline{A}\}\} \tag{4.4}$$

Also,

$$\begin{aligned}\{\underline{A}_1,f\underline{A}_2\} &= \partial^i(\underline{A}_1)(\partial_i(f)\underline{A}_2 + f\partial_i(\underline{A}_2)) - \partial^i(f)\underline{A}_2\partial_i(\underline{A}_1) - f\partial^i(\underline{A}_2)\partial_i(\underline{A}_1) \\ &\qquad + f[\underline{A}_1,\underline{A}_2] \\ &= f\{\underline{A}_1,\underline{A}_2\} + \partial_i\underline{A}_1\partial^i(f)\underline{A}_2 - \partial^i(f)\underline{A}_2\partial_i(\underline{A}_1) \\ &= f\{\underline{A}_1,\underline{A}_2\} + \partial_i(f)(\partial_i(\underline{A}_1)\underline{A}_2 - \underline{A}_2\partial_i(\underline{A}_1))\end{aligned} \tag{4.5}$$

In general, one can grind out a large number of "new" identities and operations which reduce to the familiar ones if $\mathscr{A}$ is abelian. Another possibility for the generalization of Poisson bracket is

$$\{\underline{A}_1,\underline{A}_2\}' = \partial_i(\underline{A}_1)\partial^i(\underline{A}_2) - \partial^i(\underline{A}_1)\partial_i(\underline{A}_2) \tag{4.6}$$

This one is not skew-symmetric in $\underline{A}_1,\underline{A}_2$.

Of course, the test of what is an "interesting" generalization in this area should be tied to theory of linear differential operators on vector bundles, and through that to quantum mechanics. The theory of what I call "current algebras" [4,8,11-14,20] is also closely tied in and through that to quantum field theory.

Rather than pursue these broad ramifications, I return to the immediate program developed in Section 3.

5. THE GENERALIZED POISSON BRACKET, FIRST ORDER LINEAR DIFFERENTIAL OPERATORS, AND THE SCHRÖDINGER QUANTIZATION

Continue with the notation of Section 4, and suppose in addition that $\mathscr{A}$ is an associative algebra of linear maps in a vector space V. $\mathscr{M}(R^n,V)$ then denotes the C^∞ maps $R^n \to V$. Differential operators of the form

$$\Delta = \alpha^i\partial_i + \alpha \tag{5.1}$$

with $\partial^i,\alpha^i \in \mathscr{M}(R^n,\mathscr{A})$ then map $\mathscr{M}(R^n,V) \to \mathscr{M}(R^n,V)$.

Given $\underline{A} \in \mathscr{M}(R^{2n},\mathscr{A})$ of the form

$$\underline{A} = \alpha^i(x)p_i \quad , \tag{5.2}$$

$$\alpha^i \in \mathscr{M}(R^n,\mathscr{A}) \quad ,$$

assign the differential operator

$$\Delta(\underline{A}) = \alpha^i\partial_i \tag{5.3}$$

This is the simplest example of *Schrödinger quantization.* (I want to leave open the precise question of what "quantization" means. Physically, it should mean some rule of assigning "quantum observables", i.e., linear differential operators, to "classical observables", i.e., functions.)

Let us now consider another such operator

$$\underline{B} = \beta^i p_i \tag{5.4}$$

$$\Delta(\underline{B}) = \beta^i\partial_1 \quad . \tag{5.5}$$

Then,

$$[\Delta(\underline{A}),\Delta(\underline{B})] = \alpha^i\partial_i\beta^j\partial_j - \beta^j\partial_j\alpha^i\partial_i$$

$$= \alpha^i\beta^j_i\partial_j + \alpha^i\beta^j\partial_{ij} - \beta^j\alpha^i_j\partial_i - \beta^j\alpha^i\partial_{ij}$$

$$= (\alpha^j\beta^i_j - \beta^j\alpha^i_j)\partial_i + [\alpha^i,\beta^j]\partial_{ij} \quad , \tag{5.6}$$

with $\beta^i_j = \partial_j(\beta^i)$, etc. Using (4.1),

$$\{\underline{A},\underline{B}\} = \underline{A}^i B_i - \underline{B}^i\underline{A}_i + [\underline{A},\underline{B}]$$

$$= \alpha^i\beta^j_i p_j - \beta^i\alpha^j_j p_j + [\alpha^i,\beta^j]p_{ij}$$

$$= (\alpha^j\beta^i_j - \beta^j\alpha^i_j)p_i + [\alpha^i,\beta^j]p_{ij}$$

Then, we see that:

$$\Delta(\{A,B\}) = [\Delta(A),\Delta(B)] \quad . \tag{5.7}$$

Thus, we see the simplest example of the possibility of a "quantization" scheme satisfying Dirac's dictum:

Poisson-bracket → operator commutator

for this general sort of Poisson bracket. Of course, the non-commutativity of $\mathscr{A}$ does complicate matters, and no doubt much new thought must go into a successful theory.

6. "LOCAL" AND "GLOBAL" HAMILTONIAN FORM OF DIFFERENTIAL EQUATIONS

As we have seen, the Kostant-Souriau theory provides an example of a possible "global" quantization scheme. We have seen in the previous chapter that it seems to be ideally suited to the Dirac monopole example. When we attempt to generalize from "line bundles" to "vector bundles" new complications may arise. I now want to review certain general principles.

Start off with a particle moving in an open subset of R^3 that we denote as X. Denote its coordinates as $\vec{x} = (x^i)$, $1 \leq i,j \leq 3$. Denote the dual momentum coordinates as $\vec{p} = (p_i)$. Suppose that the equations of motion are given in Hamiltonian form:

$$\frac{d\vec{x}}{dt} = h_{\vec{p}}$$

$$\frac{d\vec{p}}{dt} = -h_{\vec{x}} \tag{6.1}$$

where $H(\vec{x},\vec{p})$ is a function on R^6.

The main case to keep in mind is the *charged particle in an electromagnetic field equations*:

$$h = \frac{1}{p}(\vec{p} - \vec{a}(x))^2 + \phi(x)$$

$$= \frac{1}{2}\delta^{ij}(p_i - a_i(x))(p_j - a_j(x)) + \phi(x) \quad . \tag{6.2}$$

The "vector field" $\vec{a}(x)$ is the "vector potential" (it is really the one-differential form $a_i(x)dx^i$) and $\phi(x)$ is the "scalar potential". (Forget about the usual parameters such as masses, charges, etc.) The Hamilton equations (6.1) then take the following form:

$$\frac{dx^i}{dt} = \delta^{ij}(p_j - a_j)$$

$$\frac{dp_i}{dt} = -\partial_i(\phi)\partial_i(a_j)(p_j - a_j) \tag{6.3}$$

$$= \text{, using (6.3),}$$

$$\partial_i(a_j)\left(\delta_{jk}\frac{dx^k}{dt}\right) - \partial_i(\phi)$$

$$= \partial_i(a_j)\frac{dx^j}{dt} - \partial_i(\phi) \tag{6.4}$$

One can now eliminate the $\vec{p}$ by differentiating (6.3) once again:

$$\frac{dx^2}{dt^2} = \delta^{ij}\left(\frac{dp_j}{dt} - \partial_k(a_j)\frac{dx^k}{dt}\right)$$

$$= \text{, using (6.4),}$$

$$\delta^{ij}\left(\partial_j(a_k)\frac{dx^k}{dt} - \partial_j(\phi)\right) - \partial_k(a_i)\frac{dx^k}{dt}$$

$$= (\partial_i(a_k) - \partial_k(a_i))\frac{dx^k}{dt} - \partial_i(\phi) \quad . \tag{6.5}$$

Thus, the equations of motion in x-space can be written in coordinate-free form as

$$\frac{dx^2}{dt^2} = \left(\frac{dx}{dt} \lrcorner B\right) - E \qquad , \tag{6.6}$$

where

$$\begin{aligned} B &= d(a_i dx^i) \\ E &= d\phi \end{aligned} \tag{6.7}$$

d^2x/dt^2 is regarded as co-vectors to X using the Euclidean metric.

In order to "quantize", we must review this procedure, which requires--given B and E --finding the one-forms $a_i dx^i$ and the function ϕ. If X has non-trivial cohomology group, this may not be possible *globally*. Of course, the Kostant-Souriau procedure of quantizing via differential operators on a Hermitian line bundle is the appropriate answer in this case. However, I now want to push the reasoning back one stage.

Suppose that we are given an X as an open subset of R^3 with a given second order system of differential equations *globally* defined on X:

$$\frac{d^2\vec{x}}{dt^2} = f\left(\vec{x}, \frac{d\vec{x}}{dt}\right) \quad . \tag{6.8}$$

Suppose that this system cannot be *globally* written in the canonical form (6.2), but that it may be done so *locally*. This means that X can be covered by a collection $\{U\}$ of open subsets, with $T^d(U)$ identified as an open subset of $T^d(X)$ and with a function h^U given in each open subset $T^d(U)$, such that the projection on U of the solutions of the Hamilton equations

$$\begin{aligned} \frac{d\vec{x}}{dt} &= h^U_{\vec{p}} \\ \frac{d\vec{p}}{dt} &= - h^U_{\vec{x}} \end{aligned} \tag{6.9}$$

are the family of solutions of (6.8) which lie on U.

As we have seen in the example of the electromagnetic field, h^U may not exist *globally*. My aim is to construct a sort of "cohomology" which will generalize the Dirac magnetic monopole argument that I have reviewed in the previous chapter.

Consider the intersection $U \cap U'$ of two open subsets of the covering $\{U\}$ which covers X. Our assumption is that the projection in X of the solutions of (6.9) with h_U and $h_{U'}$ as Hamiltonians agree, and are the system of differential equations (6.8). I do not yet know how to express this condition in *general*. Instead, I will assume what I think to be a reasonable *sufficient* condition. (It might even be necessary, at least if the local Hamiltonians h_U are non-degenerate in an appropriate sense.)

Consider the cotangent bundle $T^d(U \cap U')$ as an open subset of $T^d(X)$. As for any cotangent bundle, it has a natural symplectic structure, i.e., a closed two-form ω. A *canonical transformation* is a diffeomorphism which preserves ω. A *gauge canonical transformation* is a diffeomorphism which preserves ω and which maps each cotangent space a part of x into itself. Let $G_{UU'}$ denote the group of such mappings. (Thus, $g \in G_{UU'}$ satisfies $g^*(\omega) = \omega$, and

$$g(X_x^d) = X_x^d$$

$$\text{for all } x \in U \cap U' \quad .$$

Suppose that $g \in G_{UU'}$. Set

$$h_{U'} = g^{*-1}(h_U) \quad .$$

The basic property of "canonical transformation" is that it maps solutions of Hamilton equations with Hamiltonian h_U into Hamilton equations with Hamiltonian h. The "gauge" condition means that it leaves X-projection alone. Hence, g *does not affect the system* (6.7) *resulting from projecting onto* X. Now, we make our *Basic Assumption*

> In each intersection $U \cap U'$, there is a $g_{UU'} \in G_{UU'}$ such that
>
> $$g^*_{UU'}(dh_{U'}) = dh_U \qquad (6.10)$$

I believe that in certain situations one can prove the existence of $g_{UU'}$, but I am leaving that point to the side.

With the assumption (6.10), notice that we have assigned to each pair $U, U' \in \{U\}$ such that $U \cap U'$ is non-empty, an element $g_{UU'}$ of a group $G_{UU'}$. This begins to look like a "cochain with coefficients in G", where G is some appropriately defined "abstract" group. Thus, the assumption (6.10) begins to introduce cohomology and fiber bundle theory into the game in a *natural* way. (In fact, the $\{G_U\}$, "coefficients" for the cohomology, are technically in a "sheaf of groups", but I do not want to go into that at the moment.)

The readers familiar with cohomology know that the next step is to consider the "cohomology" of the "cochain" $\{g_{UU'}\}$. Suppose U, U', U'' are three open subsets of the covering $\{U\}$. Set

$$g_{UU'U''} = g_{UU''}g_{U''U'}g_{U'U} \quad . \tag{6.11}$$

This sort of "cohomology" seems to be related to *the Dirac monopole* "quantization condition". Let us prepare the ground for this development.

7. THE "GAUGE TRANSFORMATION" OF ELECTROMAGNETISM AS A "CANONICAL GAUGE TRANSFORMATION"

Specialize the set-up described in Section 6 to the following:

$$h_U = \frac{1}{2}\delta^{ij}(p_i - a_i^U)(p_j - a_j^U) + \phi^U \tag{7.1}$$

where

$$a^U = a_i^U dx^i$$

$$\phi^U$$

are one-forms and functions (i.e., zero-forms) on U.

We know that the projection on x-space of the solutions of the Hamilton equations with Hamiltonian h_U are the *orbits of a charged particle in the electromagnetic field* whose "electric" components are $E = d\phi$ and whose "magnetic" components are $da = B$.

Thus, we see that the condition that they determine the same x-curves is that:

$$a^U - a^{U'} = df^{UU'} \tag{7.2}$$

$$\text{with } f^{UU'} \in \mathcal{F}(U \cap U') \quad ,$$

or

$$a_i^U - a_i^{U'} = \partial_i(f^{UU'}) \tag{7.3}$$

Define a map

$$g_{UU'}: T^d(U \cap U') \to T^d(U \cap U')$$

as follows:

$$g^*_{UU'}(x^i) = x^i \tag{7.4}$$

$$g^*_{UU'}(p_i) = p_i + \partial_i(f^{UU'}) \tag{7.5}$$

Then,

$$g_{UU'}(dp_i \wedge dx^i) = d(p_i + \partial_i(f^{UU'})dx^i)$$

$$= dp_i \wedge dx^i + d(df^{UU'})$$

$$= dp_i \wedge dx^i + \underset{\equiv}{0} \tag{7.6}$$

i.e., $g_{UU'}$ is *canonical.* It is also obviously a gauge transformation. (This is condition (7.4).) We also have:

$$\phi^U - \phi^{U'} = C^{UU'} \quad , \tag{7.7}$$

where $(C^{UU'})$ is a real constant. This obviously defines a one-Čech cohomology class of X, i.e., an element of

$$H^1(X,R;\ \check{C}ech) \quad . \tag{7.8}$$

(With the identification of Čech and de Rham cohomology, this is the cohomology class determined by the electric field E.) We see from (7.2) that

$$f^{UU'} - f^{UU''} - f^{U''U'} = C^{UU'U''} \tag{7.9}$$

is a *constant.* It determines a two-Čech cocycle, hence an element of

$$H^2(X,R;\ \check{C}ech) \quad .$$

(This associates with the de Rham cohomology class determined by the magnetic field B.)

<u>Remark</u>. This *topological* difference between the electric and magnetic fields--one lies in H^1, the other in H^2 --may be a clue as to why "magnetic poles" may not exist.

Now we see that condition (7.9) implies the following

$$g_{UU'U''} = \textit{identity} \quad .$$

Thus, the system $\{g_{UU'}\}$ defines a *principal fiber bundle* with structure group G = canonical gauge transformation. However, G is an *infinite dimensional group*. The condition:

> The cohomology class B determined in $H^2(X,R)$
> is integral, i.e., comes from $H^2(X,Z)$,

which is, as we have seen, essentially the Dirac "quantization" condition, i.e., just the condition that there is an "associated" principal bundle *with structure group* $U(1)$. In fact, this relation between the cohomology with coefficients in the infinite dimensional gauge group and the *finite dimensional* group $U(1)$--which is the essence of "quantization" in this situation--needs to be worked out more systematically. I will close this chapter with several topics that further prepare the ground for a full development later on.

8. THE GENERAL CANONICAL GAUGE GROUP

Suppose X is a general manifold, $T^d(X)$ is its cotangent bundle, $\omega \in \mathcal{D}^2(T^d(X))$ is the closed two-form which determines the symplectic structure on the cotangent bundle. A diffeomorphism

$$\phi: T^d(X) \to T^d(X)$$

is a *canonical "pure" gauge transformation* (for this bundle $: T^d(X) \to X$) if it satisfies the following conditions:

$$\phi^*(\omega) = \omega \tag{8.1}$$

ϕ maps each cotangent space X^d_x into itself. (8.2)

(8.2) can also be characterized by saying that the following diagram of mappings is commutative

$$\begin{array}{ccc} T^d(X) & \xrightarrow{\ \phi\ } & T^d(X) \\ \downarrow & & \downarrow \\ X & \xleftrightarrow{\text{identity}} & X \end{array}$$

(The vertical arrows are the fiber space projection maps.)

Let us now work out analytically and locally the conditions implied by (8.1) and (8.2). Let (x^i) be a coordinate system for X, $1 \leq i,j \leq n$. Let (x^i,p_i) be the corresponding canonical coordinate system for $T^d(X)$ so that:

$$\omega = dp_i \wedge dx^i \tag{8.3}$$

(8.1) and (8.2) then mean that

$$\phi^*(x^i) = x^i \tag{8.4}$$

$$dp'_i \wedge dx^i = dp_i \wedge dx^i \tag{8.5}$$

where

$$p'_i = \phi^*(p_i) \tag{8.6}$$

Hence,

$$d(p'_i - p_i) \wedge dx^i = 0 \quad .$$

This means that

$$dp'_i - dp_i = a_{ij}dx^j \tag{8.7}$$

with

$$a_{ij} = a_{ji} \quad . \tag{8.8}$$

Also,

$$d(a_{ij}dx^j) = 0 \quad . \tag{8.9}$$

(8.9) implies that

$$\frac{\partial a_{ij}}{\partial p_k} = 0 \quad . \tag{8.10}$$

Hence, there exist (at least locally) functions f_i on X such that

$$df_i = a_{ij}dx^j \quad . \tag{8.11}$$

Thus, we have:

$$d(\phi^*(p_i) - p_i) = df_i \quad .$$

We can absorb a constant into f_i so that:

$$f_i = \phi^*(p_i) - p_i \quad . \tag{8.12}$$

(8.8) implies that

$$d(f_i dx^i) = df_i \wedge dx^i = 0 \quad .$$

Hence, everything is determined (locally) by a single function $F \in \mathscr{F}(X)$ such that

$$dF = f_i dx^i$$

$$= \phi^*(p_i dx^i) - p_i dx^i \tag{8.13}$$

$$\phi^*(p_i) = p_i + \frac{\partial F}{\partial x^i} \quad . \tag{8.14}$$

Thus, for this situation, everything goes exactly as for the electromagnetic field. This gives a solid geometric foundation/interpretation of the "gauge group" that is responsible for "electric charge". Let me sum up this work in a more coordinate-free way.

Theorem 8.1. Let X be a manifold and let $T^d(X)$ be its cotangent bundle. Let $\theta \in \mathscr{D}^1(T^d(X))$ be the one-differential form which determines the contact structure, with $d\theta$ the symplectic structure. (In local coordinates, $\theta = p_i dx^i$. This one-form is actually independent of coordinates.) Let G be the group of canonical gauge transformations for the fiber space $\pi: T^d(X) \to (X)$. Then for each $g \in G$ there is a closed one-form $\eta(g)$ on X such that

$$g^*(\theta) - \theta = \pi^*(\eta(g)) \quad . \tag{8.15}$$

This assignment

$$g \to \eta(g)$$

is an isomorphism between G and the additive group of *closed* one-forms on X.

Remark. The classical mathematician (e.g., Lie) would say that G *is parameterized by one function of* n-*variables*. It is an "infinite Lie group" in the sense of Lie and Cartan. This is one of the least complex. (In particular, it is abelian.) I hope the reader can now appreciate why I believe that the theory of these groups, which has lain dormant for seventy years (except for recent work clearing up Cartan's work on the "simple" type) is one of the key ingredients in a truly *geometric* elementary particle physics.

Now, we shall indicate how these ideas may be generalized in directions that will provide the geometric foundation for the *non-abelian* gauge theories.

9. COSYMPLECTIC STRUCTURES AND GENERALIZED POISSON BRACKET

In "Interdisciplinary Mathematics", Volumes 10 and 15, I have indicated how one can define and study geometric structures that I called *cosymplectic*.

They may also be thought of as *generalized Poisson brackets*; that is the way I will study them here.

Let X be a manifold. $\mathcal{F}(X)$ denotes the associative, commutative algebra (over the real numbers) of C^{∞}, real-valued functions on X.

Definition. A *cosymplectic structure* for X is defined as an R-bilinear mapping

$$\{\ ,\ \}:\ \mathcal{F}(X)\times\mathcal{F}(X)\to\mathcal{F}(X)$$

such that

a) It defines $\mathcal{F}(X)$ as a real Lie algebra, i.e., is skew-symmetric and satisfies the Jacobi identity

b) The *derivation* property, i.e.,

$$\{f_1,f_2\,f_3\} = \{f_1,f_2\}f_3 + f_2\{f_1,f_3\}$$

for $f_1,f_2,f_3 \in \mathcal{F}(X)$.

Along with a mathematical structure, the category theorists have taught us to also think of its "morphisms", so that it forms a "category".

Definition. Let X,Y be manifolds with cosymplectic structure. A map ϕ: Y → X is a *cosymplectic homomorphism* if the pull-back map

$$\phi^*:\ \mathcal{F}(X)\to\mathcal{F}(Y)$$

is a Lie algebra homomorphism with respect to the Poisson bracket, i.e.,

$$\phi^*(\{f_1,f_2\}) = \{\phi^*(f_1),\ \phi^*(f_2)\}$$

for $f_1,f_2 \in \mathcal{F}(X)$.

Example. The *cotangent fiber bundle*. Let $Y = T^d(X)$ with the cosymplectic structure that is defined by the usual Poisson bracket. Let π: Y → X be the usual fiber space projection. In terms of the usual coordinates for $Y \equiv T^d(X)$, (x^i,p_i),

$$\{f_1,f_2\} = \frac{\partial f_1}{\partial p_i}\frac{\partial f_2}{\partial x^i} - \frac{\partial f_2}{\partial p_i}\frac{\partial f_1}{\partial x^i}$$

Put the "trivial" cosymplectic structure on X, i.e.,

$$\{f_1,f_2\} = 0$$

for $f_1,f_2 \in \mathscr{F}(X)$.

Thus, we see that the condition

$$\{x^i,x^j\} = 0$$

indicates *precisely* that π is a cosymplectic homomorphism. Objects of this sort play a basic role in the theory of "symplectic manifolds" and their application. They are sometimes also called *Lagrangian foliations* or *Lagrangian fibrations*.

This example enables us to generalize (from Section 8) the notion of "canonical gauge group" in a natural way.

10. THE CANONICAL GAUGE GROUP OF A COSYMPLECTIC FIBRATION

Let X,Y be manifolds, $\pi\colon Y \to X$ a map.

Definition. (π,Y,X) is called a *cosymplectic fibration* if the following conditions are satisfied:

a) Y and X are cosymplectic manifolds

b) π is a homomorphism of this cosymplectic structure

c) (π,Y,X) is a local-product fiber space.

The *canonical gauge group* of such a cosymplectic fibration is the group of diffeomorphisms

$$g\colon Y \to Y$$

such that:

a) g maps $\pi^{-1}(x)$ into $\pi^{-1}(x)$ for each $x \in X$, i.e., the mapping diagram

$$\begin{array}{ccc} Y & \xrightarrow{g} & Y \\ {\scriptstyle\pi}\downarrow & & \downarrow{\scriptstyle\pi} \\ X & \xrightarrow{id} & X \end{array}$$

is commutative

b) g is an automorphism of the cosymplectic structure on Y.

11. A GENERALIZATION OF THE CHARGED PARTICLE STRUCTURE

In previous sections we have seen that the equations for a charged particle in an electromagnetic field has a particularly interesting geometric structure involving "cohomology" of the canonical gauge group of the cotangent bundle. In order to be of use in elementary particle physics it would be necessary to consider gauge groups which are non-abelian. I will now show how to do this.

Suppose $\pi: Y \to X$ is a cosymplectic fibration, as defined in Section 10. Let $\{U\}$ be a covering of X by open sets. Set:

$$Y_U = \pi^{-1}(U) \quad .$$

Let G be the group of canonical group transformations, as defined in Section 10. Notice that each $g \in G$ maps each Y_U into itself. Let $h \in \mathscr{F}(Y_U)$. One can then form the vector field A_h using the cosymplectic structure:

$$A_h(f) = \{h,f\} \quad . \tag{11.1}$$

Consider the orbit curves of Y_h, i.e., the curves $t \to y(t)$ in Y_U satisfying

$$\frac{dy}{dt} = A_h(y(t)) \tag{11.2}$$

or

$$\frac{d}{dt} f(y(t)) = \{h,f\}(y(t)) \tag{11.3}$$

$$\text{for all } f \in \mathscr{F}(Y_U) \quad .$$

Suppose now that $g \in G$. Apply g to the solutions $t \to y(t)$ of (11.2), obtaining a family of curves

$$t \to g(y(t)) \quad . \tag{11.4}$$

They are orbit curves of $A_{g(h)}$, with

$$g(h) = g^{-1*}(h) \quad . \tag{11.5}$$

However, the family of curves (11.2) and (11.5) *have the same projections under* π *in* X.

Thus, we may obtain a family of curves on X which is *globally* defined in the following way. In each $U \in \{U\}$ pick an $h_U \in \mathscr{F}(Y_U)$. Suppose that in each intersection $U \cap U'$ there is a $g_{UU'} \in G$ and a $C_{UU'} \in R$ such that

$$g_{UU'}(h_{U'}) = h_U + C_{UU'} \quad . \tag{11.6}$$

The *projection of the orbits* of A_{h_U} on X are then independent of U, i.e., agree in the intersection $U \cap U'$.

The assignment

$$(U,U') \rightarrow (g_{UU'}, C_{UU'}) \quad .$$

thus defines a sort of one-cochain of the covering $\{U\}$. The development of the further topological-group theoretic machinery follows well-trodden (by topologists) lines, which I will cover in a later work in this series. Notice that it is just a generalization of the Kostant-Souriau procedure as applied above to the electromagnetic field. Now we can do quantum mechanics.

12. THE CONFIGURATION SPACE OF QUANTUM MECHANICS AS THE ORBIT SPACE OF A GAUGE GROUP

"Classical" mechanics is based geometrically on two spaces:

A *configuration space* X,

A *state* or *phase space* Y.

Usually, Y is the cotangent bundle to X. As such, it has a cosymplectic structure which determines Hamilton's equations, canonical transformation,..., i.e., all of the apparatus of *analytical mechanics*.

However, the material developed above suggests another way of looking at this. Let G be the group of gauge canonical transformations. It is a transformation group on $Y \equiv T^d(X)$. Note that

X is the orbit space of the action of G.

This enables us to immediately generalize. Let Y be any cosymplectic manifold, G a group of cosymplectic automorphisms. Set:

$X = G\backslash Y \equiv$ orbit space .

Define X as *configuration space* and proceed.

In this generality, *quantum mechanics* is included. Let $\mathcal{H}$ be a Hilbert space, i.e., a complex vector space with positive-definite inner product (,). (For the present discussion, it is useful to leave off the "completeness" axiom.) Let

$$PS(\mathcal{H})$$

be the *projective space* defined by $\mathcal{H}$, i.e., the orbit space of $\mathcal{H}-(0)$ under the action of the multiplicative group of non-zero complex numbers. $PS(\mathcal{H})$ is the *state space* of quantum mechanics.

Let G be a group of unitary transformations of $\mathcal{H}$. Since G commutes with multiplication by scalars, it acts on $PS(\mathcal{H})$.

Definition. The orbit space

$$G\backslash PS(\mathcal{H})$$

is the *configuration space*.

Let us see how this works for the standard quantum mechanical situation. Let $\vec{x}$ denote a point of R^3 with dx the usual Euclidean volume element. Let $\mathcal{H}$ be the square integrable, complex-valued function on R^3. Let G be defined as follows:

> A point of G is a measurable map
> $g: R^3 \to U(1)$.

($U(1)$ = space of complex numbers of absolute value one.) The group law for G is just point-wise multiplication. G acts on a $\psi \in \mathcal{H}$ as usual

$$(g\psi)(x) = g(x)\psi(x) \quad . \tag{12.1}$$

If we write the usual "polar" decomposition of ψ,

$$\psi = \sqrt{P}\, e^{iS/\hbar}$$

with ψ normalized so that

$$\int P(x)\, dx = 1 \quad , \qquad P \geq 0 \quad ,$$

i.e., P dx is a *probability measure*, we see that:

> The mapping $\pi: \psi \to Pdx$ has the property that the gauge group G acts *transitively* on the fiber of π. Thus, the space of probability measures on R^3 is in this natural way the *configuration space* of quantum mechanics.

Notice the fact--which is obviously rather significant--that the natural gauge group which defines the points of configuration space as orbits is the same *abstract* group in both classical and quantum mechanics, namely the group of mappings $R^3 \to R$, i.e., $\mathcal{F}(R^3)$ considered as an abelian group. In classical mechanics, this group acts as canonical transformation on R^6; in quantum mechanics, as a group of unitary operators on $L_2(R^3)(\approx\mathcal{H})$. In my papers [8,12,13] and in "Interdisciplinary Mathematics", Volume 6, I have played with general definitions of "gauge group" and their Lie algebras, and considered some ways they can act as transformation groups on finite dimensional manifolds. Unfortunately, how they can act on Hilbert spaces, e.g., as unitary operators, is very much unknown territory. (It is thought to be a very complicated question indeed!) I believe that this is a key question for elementary particle physics-quantum field theory.

One can, of course, generalize the quantum mechanical construction for particles "with spin" using Hermitian vector bundle theory. Let

$$\pi: E \to X$$

be such a bundle, with

$$\mathcal{H} = \text{space of cross-sections} \quad .$$

A *gauge transformation* may be defined (as I already pointed out in Lie Groups for Physicists) as a linear bundle automorphism g with

$$\begin{array}{ccc} E & \xrightarrow{g} & E \\ \pi\downarrow & & \downarrow\pi \\ X & \xrightarrow{id} & X \end{array}$$

a commutative diagram, such that g *preserves the Hermitian form on the fibers.*

If the dimension of the fibers π is greater than one, G will be *non-abelian*, and its properties become more complicated and interesting.

Bibliography

1. R. Hermann, "Remarks on the Geometric Nature of Quantum Phase Space", J. Math. Phys. 6 (1965), pp. 1768-1771.

2. R. Hermann, "The Second Variation for Variational Problems in Canonical Form", Bull. Amer. Math. Soc., 71 (1965), pp. 145-148.

3. R. Hermann, "Equivalence of Submanifolds of Homogeneous Spaces", Math. Ann. 158 (1965), pp. 284-289.

4. R. Hermann, Lie Groups for Physicists, W.A. Benjamin, New York, 1966.

5. R. Hermann, Differential Geometry and the Calculus of Variations, Academic Press, New York, 1969. Second edition, Math Sci Press, 1977.

Appendix A

COHOMOLOGY AND GAUGE INVARIANCE AND THE CALCULUS OF VARIATIONS FOR PARTICLE AND FIELD THEORIES

1. INTRODUCTION

In the last chapter I discussed "gauge invariance" (and associated *topological* material) generalizing the Dirac monopole story in *Hamiltonian* form. I now want to do it in "Lagrangian", i.e., calculus of variations form. This will enable us to generalize to field theories (for which the Hamiltonian formalism is awkward or non-existent).

The basic idea is that a *Lagrangian* determines a set of extremal equations, but many Lagrangians determine the same extremals. One can then envision a manifold X covered with open subsets $\{U\}$, in each of which there is a Lagrangian L_U with the property that:

> In each intersection $U \cap U'$ the extremals determined by L_U and $L_{U'}$ are the same. Thus, the extremals are *globally* defined on X, while the Lagrangian is only *locally* defined.

We see that there is the opportunity for a "cohomology" theory in this situation. Using the "Cartan form" approach to the calculus of variation puts the situation directly in de Rham cohomology terms. The Cartan form θ_{L_U} is a form in a fiber bundle with base U (an m-form if m = number of independent variables of the calculus of variations problem). The condition (*sufficient*, at any rate) that L_U and $L_{U'}$ have the same extremals is

$$d\theta_{L_U} = d\theta_{L_{U'}} \quad . \tag{1.1}$$

Thus,

$$\omega = d\theta_{L_U}$$

is a *globally* defined, closed $(m+1)$-form in a fiber bundle above X. Its cohomology class (and other related differential-geometric invariants) should be significant for physics.

We begin with the by now familiar example of the electromagnetic field. However, we shall work in the context of a general Riemannian manifold.

2. THE CARTAN FORM FOR AN ELECTROMAGNETIC FIELD IN A RIEMANNIAN MANIFOLD

Let X be a manifold of dimension n. Choose indices

$$1 \leq i,j \leq n$$

and (x^i) as local coordinates for X. (We now use general notation appropriate for differential geometry, rather than restricting ourselves to the physicist's "space-time" notation.) Thus,

$$(x^i, \dot{x}^i)$$

form a coordinate system for the tangent bundle $T(X)$. Let

$$ds^2 = g_{ij} dx^i dx^j \tag{2.1}$$

be a Riemannian metric for X. Let

$$\alpha = a_i dx^i \tag{2.2}$$

be a one-form. Set

$$L = \frac{1}{2} g_{ij} \dot{x}^i \dot{x}^j + a_i \dot{x}^i \quad . \tag{2.3}$$

Then

$$\frac{\partial L}{\partial \dot{x}^i} = g_{ij} \dot{x}^j + a_i \equiv p_i \quad . \tag{2.4}$$

<u>Remark</u>. Notice that from this "Lagrangian" point of view the "momenta" p_i are functions on $T(X)$ rather than functions of $T^d(X)$, which is the usual thing in the "symplectic manifold" appraoch.

$$h = \frac{\partial L}{\partial \dot{x}^i} \dot{x}^i - L$$

$$= g_{ij} \dot{x}^i \dot{x}^j + a_i \dot{x}^i - \frac{1}{2} g_{ij} \dot{x}^i \dot{x}^j - a_i \dot{x}^i$$

$$= g_{ij} \dot{x}^i \dot{x}^j \tag{2.5}$$

$$\theta = L dt + \frac{\partial L}{\partial \dot{x}^i} (dx^i - \dot{x}^i dt)$$

$$= \frac{\partial L}{\partial \dot{x}^i} dx^i - h\,dt \tag{2.6}$$

is the *Cartan form*. It is a one-form on $T(X) \times R$, where "R" denotes a copy of the time-interval manifold. We calculate θ readily

$$\theta = g_{ij}\dot{x}^j dx^i + \alpha - g_{ij}\dot{x}^i\dot{x}^j dt \tag{2.7}$$

3. THE SUFFICIENT CONDITION THAT TWO LAGRANGIANS OF THE TYPE OF SECTION 2 DETERMINE THE SAME EXTREMALS

Suppose

$$L' = g'_{ij}\dot{x}^i\dot{x}^j + a'_i dx^i \tag{3.1}$$

is another Lagrangian of the type considered in Section 2. Let

$$\theta' = g'_{ij}\dot{x}^j dx^i + \alpha' - g'_{ij}\dot{x}^i\dot{x}^j dt \tag{3.2}$$

be its Cartan form. The appropriate sufficient condition that they determine the same extremal curves is that

$$d\theta = d\theta' \tag{3.3}$$

Alternately (and locally) (3.3) means that there is a function $f(x,\dot{x},t)$ on $T(X) \times R$ such that:

$$df = \theta - \theta' \quad . \tag{3.4}$$

Thus,

$$\frac{\partial f}{\partial \dot{x}^i} = 0 \tag{3.5}$$

since neither θ nor θ' involve dx^i. But,

$$\frac{\partial f}{\partial t} = (g'_{ij} - g_{ij})\dot{x}^i\dot{x}^j \quad , \tag{3.6}$$

This is compatible with (3.5) only if

$$g'_{ij} = g_{ij} \quad .$$

Thus,

$$\theta - \theta' = \alpha - \alpha' \quad . \tag{3.7}$$

This leads to the following way of putting it:

Theorem 3.1. Let two Riemannian metrics and two one-forms be given on X. Form the Lagrangian as above. They satisfy (3.3) if and only if the metrics are equal and

$$d(\alpha - \alpha') = 0 \quad . \tag{3.8}$$

4. THE COHOMOLOGY CLASS ASSOCIATED WITH "GAUGE INVARIANCE" OF LAGRANGIANS

Let X be a manifold covered with a family $\{U\}$ of open subsets. The tangent bundle $T(U)$ to each such U is an open subset of $T(X)$. For each real valued function $L: T(U) \to R$ we can define its Cartan form θ as a one-form on $T(U) \times R$.

Let us suppose that in each U we are given a Lagrangian L_U, that $\theta_U \in \mathcal{D}^1(T(U)) \times R)$ is the Cartan form, and that in the intersection

$$U \cap U' \quad ,$$

$$d(\theta_U - \theta_{U'}) \quad . \tag{4.1}$$

Then we know that the extremal curves of L_U are *really independent of* U, i.e., are globally defined on X. There is a two-form ω on $T(X) \times R$ such that

$$\omega = d\theta_U \tag{4.2}$$

in each open subset U. ω defines a de Rham cohomology class,

$$H^2(T(X) \times R) \quad .$$

It is the basic object. Call it the *gauge cohomology class.*

Suppose that the Lagrangians L are all of "electromagnetic type" considered in Sections 2 and 3. This means that X has a *globally defined* Riemannian metric, and in each U a one-form α^U, with

$$d(\alpha^U - \alpha^{U'}) = 0$$

in the intersection $U \cap U'$ of two open subsets of the covering. We can then define a two-form ω' on X such that

$$\omega' = d\alpha^U \tag{4.3}$$

in each open subset U. Let $\pi: T(X) \times R \to X$ be the projection map. Note that

$$\pi^*(\omega') = \omega \quad . \tag{4.4}$$

Then the two-cohomology class defined by ω' in $H^2(X,R)$ pulls back under π to give the *gauge cohomology class* of the variational problem.

Again, if the cohomology class determined by ω or ω' has *integral* periods, we are in business--according to the Kostant-Souriau theory--for "quantization". This could lead back to the standard Dirac monopole quantization theory, but I will not pursue that here.

5. A FIELD-THEORETIC GENERALIZATION

All of this *generalizes* to field theories (via the extension of the Cartan form formalism presented in my previous books) and should be interesting for elementary particle physics. In order to get into this with a minimum dealy, I will switch over to the physicists' notation. Consider "fields" ϕ^a, which are functions of space-time variables

$$x^\mu \quad , \qquad 0 \le \mu,\nu \le 3 \ , \qquad 0 \le a,b \le m$$

Warning. The x's have a completely different meaning here from the previous sections. Here they are "independent" variables, there they were "dependent", to use the classical terminology.

Let ϕ^a_μ denote the "derivation" of the field. Thus, (x,ϕ^a,ϕ^a_μ) are the natural coordinates on $J^1(R^4,R^m)$, the one-jets (in the Ehresmann sense) of mappings $R^4 \to R^m$. If $L(x, \ , \ )$ is a function of these variables, consider the calculus of variations problem of extremizing

$$\int L\, dx \quad ,$$

where

$$dx = dx^0 \wedge \cdots \wedge dx^3 \quad .$$

The *Cartan form*

$$\theta = L dx + \frac{\partial L}{\partial \phi^a_\mu} (d\phi^a - \phi^a_\nu dx^\nu) \wedge (\partial_\mu \lrcorner\, dx) \quad . \tag{5.1}$$

Let the (ϕ^a) be coordinates of a space Y. (Physically, it is the "internal symmetry" space.) Suppose that Y is covered with the open subset $\{U\}$ (with the "independent variables" globally defined), and with such Lagrangian L^U defined in each open subset $U \in \{U\}$, *but in the intersection having the same extremals.* Thus, the extremal equations

$$\frac{\partial}{\partial x^\mu}\left(\frac{\partial L}{\partial \phi^a_\mu}\right) = \frac{\partial L}{\partial \phi^a} \tag{5.2}$$

are *globally* defined, i.e., define a family of maps $X \to Y$ independent of the covering of Y.

Thus, we obtain in each U a Cartan form

$$\theta^U = L^U dx + \frac{\partial L^U}{\partial \phi^a_\mu} (d\phi^a - \phi^a dx^\nu) \wedge (\partial_\mu \lrcorner\, dx)$$

Let us *suppose* that in $U \cap U'$,

$$d(\theta^U - \theta^{U'}) = 0 \quad . \tag{5.3}$$

This guarantees that the extremal equations agree in $U \cap U'$.

Let us now specialize U to be of the following form

$$L^U = \frac{1}{a} A^{\mu\nu}_{ab}(\phi)\phi^a_\mu \phi^b_\nu + A^{\mu,U}(\phi)\phi^a_\mu \tag{5.4}$$

Note that we *assume* that the highest order coefficients $A^{\mu\nu}_{ab}(\phi)$ are independent of U, i.e., define a *globally* geometric structure on Y. However, the $\{A^{\mu,U}_a\}$ vary. It is this term that has the "gauge" property. Then,

$$\frac{\partial L^U}{\partial \phi^a_\mu} = A^{\mu\nu}_{ab}\phi^b_\nu + A^{\mu,U}_a \tag{5.5}$$

$$\theta^U = L^U dx + (A^{\mu\nu}_{ab}\phi^b_\nu + A^{\mu,U}_a)(d\phi^a - \phi^a_\nu dx^\nu) \wedge (\partial_\mu \lrcorner\, dx)$$

Thus in $U \cap U'$,

$$\theta^U - \theta^{U'} = (A^{\mu,U}_a - A^{\mu,U'}_a)\phi^a dx + (A^{\mu,U}_a - A^{\mu,U'}_a)(d\phi^a - \phi^a_\nu dx^\nu) \wedge (\partial_\mu \lrcorner\, dx) \tag{5.6}$$

We can express the condition

$$d(\theta^U - \theta^{U'}) = 0$$

in a more classical way. Using the results of Geometry, Physics and Systems, it is equivalent to the following condition:

The Euler equations are *identities* for the Lagrangian

$$L^U - L^{U'} \quad .$$

But,

$$L^U - L^{U'} = (A_a^{\mu,U}(\phi) - A_a^{\mu,U'})\phi_\mu^a \quad .$$

The Euler equations are:

$$\begin{aligned} 0 &= \partial_\mu(A_a^{\mu,U} - A_a^{\mu,U'}) - \partial_a(A_b^{\mu,U} - A_b^{\mu,U'})\partial_\mu\phi^b \\ &= (\partial_b(A_a^{\mu,U}) - \partial_b(A_a^{\mu,U'}))\partial_\mu\phi^b - (\partial_a(A_b^{\mu,U}) - \partial_a(A_b^{\mu,U'}))\partial_\mu\phi^b \end{aligned} \tag{5.7}$$

for <u>all</u> functions $\phi^b(x)$. These conditions then mean that:

$$d((A_a^{\mu,U}) - A_a^{\mu,U})d\phi^a) = 0 \quad . \tag{5.8}$$

Thus, we can define a set ω^μ of *globally-defined*, closed two-forms in Y by saying that in each open subset U,

$$\omega^\mu = d(A_a^{\mu,U}d\phi^a) \quad . \tag{5.9}$$

Their cohomology classes play the same role that the cohomology class determined by the electromagnetic field plays in the Dirac monopole theory.

In this section we have chosen the simplest direct generalization of the "particle" calculus of variations situation. After this practice, we can move on to territory which is more interesting physically.

6. INTO YANG-MILLS LAND

Keep the notation of Section 5, but change the hypothesis about each L^U to the following

$$L^U = \frac{1}{a} A_{ab}^{\mu\nu}(\phi_\mu^a - B_\mu^{a,U})(\phi_\nu^b - B_\nu^{b,U}) + A_a^\mu(\phi_\mu^a - B_\mu^{a,U}) \quad . \tag{6.1}$$

The $A_{ab}^{\mu,\nu}, A_a^\mu$ are functions of ϕ, and are independent of U. The $B_\mu^{a,U}$ are also functions of ϕ, but they vary with U. They are the *Yang-Mills fields*.

<u>Remark</u>. Usually, the Yang-Mills fields are interpreted geometrically as *connections*. This is a slightly different approach. We are not starting off with a *postulate* about how they transform on $U \cap U'$, which is what we would do if we adopted the connection point of view. The approach to be used here is more analogous to "cohomology".

Let us work out the Cartan form for a Lagrangian of type (6.1). (Keep in mind that the ϕ^a are the *field* variables. We are not regarding the B^a as "independent" fields, but as functions of the fields which are *given* in each open subset U.)

In the intersection $U \cap U'$, we must find the conditions that the Euler equations for $L^U - L^{U'}$ are an *identity*. This is what the "gauge invariance" condition amounts to. To simplify the calculations, let us suppose that the following condition is satisfied:

$$\boxed{\text{The } A^{\mu,\nu}_{ab},\ A^{\mu}_{a} \text{ are constants.}} \tag{6.2}$$

Then

$$\frac{\partial L^U}{\partial \phi^a_\mu} = A^{\mu\nu}_{ab}(\phi^b_\nu - B^{b,U}_\nu) + A^\mu_a$$

$$\frac{\partial L^U}{\partial \phi^a} = -A^{\mu\nu}_{bc}(\phi^b_\mu - B^{b,U}_\mu)\partial_a(B^{c,U}_\nu) - A^\mu_b \partial_a(B^{b,U}_\mu)$$

$$\partial_\mu\left(\frac{\partial L^U}{\partial \phi^a_\mu}\right) = A^{\mu\nu}_{ab}(\phi^b_{\mu\nu} - \partial_a(B^{b,U}_\nu)\partial_\mu(\phi^c))$$

Hence, the Euler equations being identities for $L^U - L^{U'}$ means that:

$$\begin{aligned} -A^{\mu\nu}_{ab}\partial_c(B^{b,U}_\nu - B^{b,U'}_\nu)\phi^c_\mu = {} & -A^{\mu\nu}_{bc}((\phi^b_\mu - B^{b,U}_\mu)\partial_a(B^{c,U}_\nu) \\ & - (\phi^b_\mu - B^{b,U'}_\mu)\partial_a(B^{c,U'}_\nu)) \\ & - A^\mu_b(\partial_a(B^{b,U}_\mu) - \partial_a(B^{b,U'}_\mu)) \end{aligned} \tag{6.3}$$

Notice that the second derivatives of ϕ^a have cancelled out.

In equating this expression, we now regard the ϕ^a_μ as *independent* variables. (This is what we mean by saying that the "Euler equations are identities".) This requires that:

$$\boxed{A^{\mu\nu}_{ab}\partial_c(B^{b,U}_\nu - B^{b,U'}_\nu) = A^{\mu\nu}_{cb}(\partial_a(B^{b,U}_\nu) - \partial_a(B^{b,U'}_\nu))} \tag{6.4}$$

and

$$A^{\mu\nu}_{bc}(B^{b,U}_{\mu}\partial_a(B^{c,U}_{\nu}) - B^{b,U'}_{\mu}\partial_a(B^{c,U'}_{\mu})) = A^{\mu}_{b}(\partial_a(B^{b,U}_{\mu}) - \partial_a(B^{b,U'}_{\mu}))$$

Set:

$$F^{U}_{a} = A^{\mu}_{b}\partial_a(B^{b,U}_{\mu}) - A^{\mu\nu}_{bc}B^{b,U}_{\mu}\partial_a(B^{c,U}_{\nu}) \tag{6.5}$$

$$G^{\mu,U}_{ac} = A^{\mu\nu}_{ab}\partial_c(B^{b,U}_{\nu}) - A^{\mu\nu}_{cb}\partial_a(B^{b,U}_{\nu}) \tag{6.6}$$

Notice that the $(F^{U}_{a}, G^{\mu,U}_{ac})$ result from applying a nonlinear differential operator (which is independent of U') to the "potentials" $B^{a,U}_{\mu}$. In the intersection $U \cap U'$,

$$F^{U}_{a} = F^{U'}_{a}$$

$$G^{\mu,U}_{ac} = G^{\mu,U'}_{ac} \quad .$$

Thus, we are in a position to define a "nonlinear" cohomology, patterened after what was done in earlier chapters for the electromagnetic-Dirac case. I will leave the subject at this point for a later volume.

Appendix B

A COORDINATE-FREE DESCRIPTION OF THE "LOCAL" CALCULUS OF VARIATIONS THEORY AND ITS ASSOCIATED GAUGE AND COHOMOLOGY THEORY

1. INTRODUCTION

So far, I have been tentatively probing beyond the basic Dirac monopole argument in order to feel my way toward a general framework. With this work in hand, it is appropriate to attempt a synthesis of the ideas. As I have stated before, I believe that this material has new mathematical import (a "nonlinear cohomology") and is quite basic to elementary particle physics.

2. THE CARTAN FUNCTOR

For each manifold X let

$$M(X) = T(X) \times R \quad . \tag{2.1}$$

(More intrinsically, $M(X)$ = one-jets of mappings $R \to X$.) Fix a volume element form for X. Then, to each function

$$L: M(X) \to M$$

there is a one-form

$$\theta(L) \in \mathscr{D}^1(M(X)) \quad ,$$

called the *Cartan form.* L is called a *Lagrangian* for X. This correspondence

$$L \to \theta(L)$$

is the *Cartan functor*, and is the basic one in the *geometric* theory of the calculus of variations.

This generalizes to field theories. Replace R with a manifold Y so that

$$M(X) = \text{one-jets of mappings } Y \to X$$

$$\theta(L) \in \mathscr{D}^r(M(X)) \ , \qquad \text{where } r = \dim L.$$

3. "LOCAL" VARIATIONAL PROBLEMS

Continue with X as a manifold

$$M = T(X) \times R \quad .$$

(For simplicity, we restrict attention to the "particle", i.e., one-independent variable situations.) Let X have a covering

$$\{U\}$$

by open subsets. $T(U)$ is then an open subset of $T(X)$. Set

$$M(U) = T(U) \times R \quad .$$

This determines an open covering $\{M(U)\}$ of $M(X)$.

Definition. A *local variational problem* for X (relative to this open covering) is defined as an assignment

$$U \to L_U : M(U) \to R$$

of a Lagrangian function to each $U \in \{U\}$.

Remark. In terms of the "cohomology" interpretation I am developing, this should be thought of as an *0-cochain*.

Definition. Let $U \to L_U$ be a local variational problem. For each $U,U' \in \{U\}$ which intersect, set

$$\omega_{U,U'} = d\theta(L_U) - d\theta(L_{U'}) \quad . \tag{3.1}$$

$\omega_{U,U'}$, an element of $\mathscr{D}^2(M(U) \wedge M(U'))$ whose exterior derivative is zero, defines a two-Čech cochain with coefficients in the sheaf of two-forms on $M(X)$.

Definition. The local variational problem $\{L_U\}$ is said to define a *global extremal system* if

$$\omega_{U,U'} = 0 \tag{3.2}$$

for each $U,U' \in \{U\}$ which intersect. The *extremals* are then the curves

$$t \to x(t)$$

in X whose prolonged curves

$$t \to \left(x, \frac{dx}{dt}, t\right)$$

are Cauchy characteristic curves for each $d\theta(L_U)$.

Remark. This suggests a "weaker" cohomology theory that might be interesting. Replace condition (3.2) by the following one:

> $d\theta(L_U)$ and $d\theta(L_{U'})$ have the same Cauchy characteristic curves.

Define the extremals as the projection into X of the Cauchy characteristics. I will not pursue such a theory at the moment.

Suppose (3.2) is satisfied. We will then say that the local variational problem $\{L_U\}$ is *gauge-invariant*. One can define a closed one-form ω on $M(X)$ as follows

$$\omega = d\theta(L_U) \tag{3.3}$$

in each open subset $M(U)$. ω is called the *curvature form* of the *gauge-invariant local variational problem.*

Remark. I am not happy with this use of the term "gauge invariant", but cannot think of a better term right now. I reserve the possibility to change it later.

4. EQUIVALENCE OF TWO LOCAL VARIATIONAL PROBLEMS

Let X continue as a manifold--physically, the *configuration space*. Let $\{U\}$ be a fixed open covering of X. Set: $M(U) = T(U) \times R$. Consider a gauge-invariant local variational problem

$$\{L_U\} \quad .$$

Recall that this means that L_U is a real-valued function in each open subset $M(U)$, and that, in the intersection $M(U) \cap M(U')$, for two open subsets $U, U' \in \{U\}$,

$$d\theta_{L_U} = d\theta_{L_{U'}} \quad .$$

Definition. Consider two such gauge-invariant local variational problems $\{L_U\}$, $\{L_{U'}\}$. They are said to be *equivalent* if there is a globally-defined Lagrangian function

$$L\colon T(X) \times R \to R$$

such that in each $U \in \{U\}$,

$$\theta_{L_U} - \theta_{L_{U'}} = \theta_L \quad . \tag{4.1}$$

This condition then implies that the *curvature-forms* ω, ω' of the two local problems are cohomologous in the de Rham cohomology sense.

We are particularly interested in knowing when a given local, gauge-invariant variational problem $\{L_U\}$ is equivalent--in the above sense--to one whose curvature form is the pull-back of a form on the base space X. Notice that this is what happens in the electromagnetic field case:

X = Riemannain manifold

ω = closed, two-form on X. $\langle , \rangle$ denotes inner product on tangent vectors

$\{U\}$ is a covering such that in each U there is a one-form α_U such that $d\alpha_U = \omega$.

$$L_U(v) = \langle v,v\rangle^{1/2} + \alpha_U(v)$$

$$L(v) = \langle v,v\rangle^{1/2} \quad .$$

5. THE CHARACTERISTIC CLASS OF A GAUGE-INVARIANT LOCAL VARIATIONAL PROBLEM

Let (x^i), $1 \leq i,j \leq n$, be local coordinates for the manifold X. Let $(x^i, \dot{x}^i)$ be the corresponding coordinates for $T(X)$, i.e.,

$$x^i(v) = x^i(\pi(v))$$

where $\pi: T(X) \to X$ is the bundle projection

$$\dot{x}^i(v) = dx^i(v) \quad .$$

Let $L: T(X) \times R \to R$ be a Lagrangian of L with $\theta(L)$ its Cartan form. Thus $d\theta(L) = 0$ if and only if the Euler extremal equations

$$\frac{d}{dt}\left(\frac{\partial L}{\partial \dot{x}^i}\right) = \frac{\partial L}{\partial x^i} \tag{5.1}$$

are *identities*.

Let us work out the condition that $d\theta(L) = 0$ in more detail. (5.1) becomes

$$\frac{\partial^2 L}{\partial \dot{x}^i \partial t} + \frac{\partial^2 L}{\partial \dot{x}^j \partial \dot{x}^i} \frac{d^2 x^j}{dt^2} + \frac{\partial^2 L}{\partial x^j \partial \dot{x}^i} \frac{dx^j}{dt} = \frac{\partial L}{\partial x^i}\left(x, \frac{dx}{dt}, t\right) \tag{5.2}$$

In order that these be *identities*, we must then have:

$$\frac{\partial^2 L}{\partial \dot{x}^i \partial \dot{x}^j} = 0 \quad , \tag{5.3}$$

since this is the only term that contains d^2x/dt^2. (5.3) implies that L is of the form:

$$L = a_i(x,t)\dot{x}^i \quad . \tag{5.4}$$

Thus, L is the Lagrangian associated with the t-dependent one-form

$$\alpha = a_i \, dx^i \quad \text{on } X \quad .$$

(5.2) now takes the following form:

$$\frac{\partial a_i}{\partial t} + \partial_j(a_i)\dot{x}^j = \partial_i(a_j)\dot{x}^j \quad .$$

In order that this be an identity, we must have

$$\frac{\partial a_i}{\partial t} = 0$$

$$d\alpha = 0 \quad .$$

We can now sum up as follows.

Theorem 5.1. Let $L: T(X) \times R \to R$ be a Lagrangian function for X such that all curves in X are its extremals. Then L derives from a closed one-form α in X, i.e.,

$$L(v) = \alpha(v)$$

$$\text{for all } v \in T(X) \quad .$$

$\theta(L)$ is then $\pi^*(\alpha)$, where $\pi: T(X) \to R$ is the fiber space projection.

Thus, we can reformulate the notion of a local, gauge-invariant variational problem. We are to be given a manifold X, an open covering $\{U\}$, with a Lagrangian $L_U: T(U) \times R \to R$ given on each U, such that:

$$d(\theta(L_U) - \theta(L_{U'})) = 0$$

on each intersection. But,

$$\theta(L_U) - \theta(L_{U'}) = \theta(L_U - L_{U'}) \quad .$$

By Theorem 5.1,

$$\theta(L_U - L_{U'}) = \pi^*(\alpha_{UU'}) \quad , \tag{5.5}$$

where

$$\alpha_{U,U'}$$

is a *closed* two-form in $U \cap U'$. This assignment

$$(U,U') \to \alpha_{UU'}$$

defines a one-cochain of X (strictly, with respect to the covering $\{U\}$) *with coefficients* in the sheaf of differential forms on X. (See Hirzebruch [ ] for the details of sheaf-cohomology in this approach. I will not use any of the fancier versions that come in later.) It is a *closed* cochain, i.e.,

$$\alpha_{UU'} = \alpha_{UU''} + \alpha_{U''U'} \tag{5.6}$$

for $U, U', U'' \in \{U\}$, which intersect.

Since the sheaf of two-differential forms on X is *fine*, we can write

$$\alpha_{UU'} = \beta_U - \beta_{U'} \quad , \tag{5.7}$$

where $\{\beta_U\}$ is an assignment of a one-form on U for each $U \in \{U\}$. Since

$$\alpha\alpha_{UU'} = 0$$

we have:

$$d\beta_U = d\beta_{U'} \quad . \tag{5.8}$$

Thus, we can define a closed two-form ω on X such that

$$\omega = d\beta_U \tag{5.9}$$

in each open subset $U \in \{U\}$. ω is *base-curvature* form determined by the local-gauge invariant variational problem. Its de Rham cohomology class is called its *characteristic class*.

We can now follow the Kostant-Souriau "quantization" procedure, if the cohomology class determined by ω comes from an integral cocycle, i.e., an element of $H^2(X,Z)$. As we have seen in a previous chapter, this involves construction of a complex Hermitian line bundle on X whose curvature is ω. This will enable us to discuss "quantization" of local, gauge-invariant variational problems (from this "Lagrangian" point of view). However, I will not go into detail at this point.

Appendix C

LOCAL GAUGE-INVARIANT LAGRANGE VARIATIONAL PROBLEMS

1. INTRODUCTION

This formalism described in the preceding appendix is capable of extensive expansion and generalization which might have broad ramifications in science and technology. In this appendix I will briefly discuss one form such a generalization might take to the general *Lagrange problem* of the calculus of variations. In turn, this is closely related to the *optimal control variational problem*, the knowledge of which is now widespread in engineering circles (although physicists are mostly ignorant of it). I will follow the approach in my paper "Some Differential Geometric Aspects of the Lagrange variational problem" with the "local", "gauge-invariant" aspect as a new feature. Then I will specialize to the "optimal control" situation.

2. GENERALITIES ABOUT THE LAGRANGE VARIATIONAL PROBLEM

Let X be a manifold, $T(X)$ its tangent bundle. A *Lagrange variational problem* (or a *constrained variational problem*) is defined by the following data:

a) A function $L: T(X) \to R$

b) A submanifold $C \subset T(X)$, called the *constraint submanifold.*

Remark. For simplicity, we will not consider time-dependency problems.

The *variational problem* defined by L and C is to extremize

$$\int_a^k L\left(x(t), \frac{dx}{dt}\right) dt \tag{2.1}$$

over all curves $t \to x(t)$ in X with the end-points fixed and

$$\left(x(t), \frac{dx}{dt}\right) \in C \tag{2.2}$$

for all t.

(2.2) is the new and complicating factor.

Here is how to set up the extremals in terms of differential forms in local coordinates. Let

$$(x^i) \quad , \qquad 1 \le i,j \le n$$

be a local coordinate system for X. Let $(x^i, \dot{x}^i)$ be the associated coordinate system for $T(X)$. Suppose the constraints C are determined by equations of the form

$$f_a(x,\dot{x}) = 0 \quad , \qquad 1 \leq a,b \leq m \quad . \tag{2.3}$$

Introduce new variables λ^a.

$$\theta(L) = L\,dt + \frac{\partial L}{\partial \dot{x}^i}(dx^i - \dot{x}^i dx) \tag{2.4}$$

$$\theta(f_a) = f_a dt + \frac{\partial f_a}{\partial \dot{x}^i}(dx^i - \dot{x}^i dt) \quad . \tag{2.5}$$

Set:

$$\theta = \theta(L) + \lambda^a \theta(f_a) \tag{2.6}$$

restricted to the submanifold Y defined by (2.3) of the manifold

$$T(X) \times R \times R^m \quad .$$

The *extremals* are then the curves

$$t \to y(t)$$

in Y which are Cauchy characteristic for $d\theta$, i.e., which are such that

$$\frac{dy}{dt} \lrcorner\, d\theta = 0 \quad , \tag{2.7}$$

where $t \to dy/dt$ denotes the tangent vector curves to y.

The "global" version of this can be described as follows:

Y = the normal vector bundle to the submanifold $C \times R$ of the manifold $T(X) \times R$.

3. LOCAL, GAUGE-INVARIANT LAGRANGE VARIATIONAL PROBLEMS

Suppose now that X is a manifold with a covering $\{U\}$ by open subsets. Then $T(U) \times R$ is an open subset of $T(X) \times R$. Suppose a Lagrange variational problem is given in U, i.e., a Lagrangian function L_U and a constraint subset $C_U \subset T(X)$. They determine a family of curves in U called the *extremals*.

Set

$M(U)$ = normal vector bundle to subset $C_U \times R$ of $T(X) \times R$.

In local coordinates, $M(U)$ is the space of variables $(x,\dot{x},t,\lambda)$ constrained by relations of the form

$$f_a^U(x,\dot{x},t,\lambda) = 0 \quad .$$

One can form the Cartan form on $M(U)$

$$\theta^U = \theta(L_U) + \lambda^a\theta(f^U) \quad . \tag{3.1}$$

The extremal curves are the projection onto X of the Cauchy characteristic curves of the two-form $d\theta^U$.

Definition. These data define a local, gauge-invariant Lagrange variational problem if

$$d\theta^U = d\theta^{U'} \tag{3.2}$$

in the interaction $M(U) \cap M(U')$, for each pair U,U' of open subsets of the covering $\{U\}$ which intersect.

We can now reformulate this structure into a more elegant framework.

4. A REFORMULATION IN TERMS OF THE THEORY OF CAUCHY CHARACTERISTIC-SYMPLECTIC FOLIATIONS

Here is a framework which seems general enough to include the situation considered in this chapter and the previous one. Let Y,X be manifolds with $\pi: Y \to X$ a fiber space map. Suppose given a closed two-form ω on Y. A curve $t \to y(t)$ in Y is *Cauchy characteristic* for ω if

$$\frac{dy}{dt} \lrcorner\, \omega = 0.$$

A curve t $x(t)$ in X is an *extremal* if it is of the form

$$x(t) = \pi(y(t)) \tag{4.1}$$

where $t \to y(t)$ is a Cauchy characteristic curve in M.

It is obviously challenging to quantum mechanics to develop a theory of "quantization" which is adequate to handle such situations in a reasonably general way. Of course, such a theory should encompass the topological aspects of Dirac's monopole theory.

We will call the geometric structure defined by the extremal curves X an *extremal system*. Here is another general method for defining such systems.

5. EXTREMAL SYSTEMS DEFINED BY GROUPS OF GAUGE TRANSFORMATIONS--SYMPLECTIC AUTOMORPHISMS

Let Y be a manifold with a closed two-form ω. Let

$$\pi: Y \to X$$

be a submersion. The Cauchy characteristics define curves in Y; projected down to X by π they define an *extremal system* as explained in Section 4.

We have seen in our earlier treatment of the Dirac monopole that there is an additional feature--an infinite dimensional group of "gauge transformations". In order to put this into the general structure being constructed in this chapter, we can postulate an additional feature.

A diffeomorphism $g: Y \to Y$ is a *symplectic automorphism* if

$$g^*(\omega) = \omega \quad .$$

Warning. I am not assuming that ω is a non-degenerate two-form, so that it does not define a "symplectic structure" in the usual sense of the recent mathematical literature. However, the names and definitions in this subject are so confusing, ambiguous and subjective that they probably can never be straightened out completely. After all, the whole subject is two hundred years old (dating it, say, from Lagrange's "Méchanique analytique") and probably can never be completely rationalized in the same way as other branches of mathematics have been.

We can now *postulate a group* G *of symplectic automorphisms of* (Y,ω) *whose orbits are the fibers of* π.

Let us now look at this from a "local" point of view.

6. FIBER SPACES WITH A LOCAL HAMILTONIAN STRUCTURE

Let Y be a $(2n+1)$-dimensional manifold with a closed two-form ω on Y of maximal rank, i.e., such that

$$(d\omega)^n \neq 0 \quad . \tag{6.1}$$

The Cauchy characteristics of ω are then one-dimensional. We suppose that

a) $\pi: Y \to X$ is a local-product fiber space

b) X is an n-dimensional manifold.

c) There is a *global time function* on Y.

d) X can be covered by open subsets $\{U\}$

e) In each $U \in \{U\}$, there is a coordinate system (x^i_U).

f) $\pi^{-1}(U)$ has a coordinate system formed of functions $(\pi^*(x^i_U),\ p^U_i,\ t$

g) In each $\pi^{-1}(U)$, there is a function h_U such that

$$\omega = dp^U_i \wedge d\pi^*(x^i_U) - dh_U \wedge dt \tag{6.2}$$

h) In the intersection $\pi^{-1}(U) \cap \pi^{-1}(U')$, for $U,U' \in \{U\}$, the p^U_i are functions $F^{UU'}_i$ of $(x^i_{U'}, p^i_{U'})$.

Thus, on each open subset $\pi^{-1}(U)$ of Y the Cauchy characteristics of ω take the following Hamiltonian form:

$$\begin{aligned} \frac{dx_U}{dt} &= \frac{\partial h}{\partial p^U} \\ \frac{dp^U}{dt} &= -\frac{\partial h}{\partial x_U} \end{aligned} \tag{6.3}$$

The projection into X are the *extremals*.

Remark. Caratheodory proves in his book *Variationsrechnung* that conversely each family of curves in X definable by Hamilton equations of type (6.3) is the set of extremals of a Lagrange variational problem. Thus this is an appropriate setting for the study of local, gauge-invariant Lagrange variational problems.

With this situation, we see that the group of diffeomorphisms

$$Y \to Y$$

$$p_i \to p_i + \frac{\partial f}{\partial x^i}$$

$$t \to t$$

where f is a function of x alone, is the appropriate group gauge transformation (and symplectic automorphism) which acts transitively in the fibers of π.

7. OPTIMAL CONTROL VARIATIONAL PROBLEMS

The "optimal control" problem is a special form of the Lagrange problem. Its theory has now become much better known than the classical Lagrange problem theory, because it is especially suited to applications in a wide variety of disciplines. The Pontryagin maximal principle (which is beautiful as a form of the classical "first order necessary conditions") and the Hamilton-Jacobi-Bellman equation (related to the classical "sufficient conditions" and "extremal fields") wrap up much of the classical theories in a nice bundle.

I will now have to change notation in order to conform more closely to that used in the control literature. Suppose X and U are manifolds with coordinates

$$(x^i) \quad , \qquad 1 \le i,j \le n \quad ;$$

$$(u^a) \quad , \qquad 1 \le a,b \le m \quad .$$

X is called the *state space*, U the *input space*.

The *optimal control problem* is to extremize

$$\int L(x(t),u(t))\, dt \tag{7.1}$$

subject to the constraint

$$\frac{dx}{dt} = f(x,u) \quad . \tag{7.2}$$

In order to handle this with differential-geometric techniques, introduce another space Λ with variables (λ_i) (called the *costate space*). Set:

$$M = X \times U \times \Lambda \times T$$

(T is R, the space whose variable is t.) Set:

$$\theta = Ldt + \lambda_i(dx^i - f^i dt) \quad . \tag{7.3}$$

θ is our old friend, the *Cartan form* adapted to this situation. It is a one-form on M. The *extremals* are again the Cauchy characteristic covers of $d\theta$. (However, $d\theta$ does not have constant rank.) Let us work that out. Set:

$$h = L - \lambda_i f^i \quad . \tag{7.4}$$

h might be called the *Pontryagin-Hamilton function*. Then

$$\theta = hdt + \lambda_i dx^i$$

$$d\theta = \left(\frac{\partial h}{\partial u^a} du^a + \frac{\partial h}{\partial x^i} dx^i + \frac{\partial h}{\partial \lambda i} d\lambda_i\right) \wedge dt + d\lambda_i \wedge dx^i$$

Let $p \in M$. In order that there be a nonzero Cauchy characteristic vector at p, one must have $\partial h/\partial u^a(p) = 0$. This is the "maximal principle".

Assume the conditions

$$\frac{\partial h}{\partial u^a} = 0$$

Define a submanifold of M; call it N. On N,

$$d\theta = d\lambda_i \wedge dx^i + dh \wedge dt$$

The Cauchy characteristic curves of $d\theta$ are then the curves $t \to x(t), u(t), (t)$ in M satisfying the following "mixed" set of differential and "algebraic" equations"

$$\boxed{\begin{aligned} \frac{\partial h}{\partial u^a} &= 0 \\ \frac{dx}{dt} &= -\frac{\partial h}{\partial \lambda} \\ \frac{d\lambda}{dt} &= -\frac{\partial h}{\partial x} \end{aligned}} \qquad (7.4)$$

Now, we turn to what the physicist calls "gauge invariance" in this context.

<u>Definition</u>. Consider two optimal control problems with the same input and state space, characterized by functions (L,f), (L',f'). Let θ, θ' be their Cartan forms. The variational problems are said to be *equivalent* if

$$d\theta = d\theta' \quad . \qquad (7.5)$$

Appendix D

MAXWELL AND YANG-MILLS EQUATIONS IN TERMS OF DIFFERENTIAL FORMS AND THE VARIATIONAL FORMALISM

by Frank Estabrook, Robert Hermann, and Hugo Wahlquist

1. INTRODUCTION

Estabrook and Harrison have shown in [1] that Maxwell's equations can be written very elegantly in terms of differential forms, i.e., exterior differential systems. (This is also very useful, e.g., in the search for symmetries.) We will now show how this description may be obtained via the usual variational principle *and* the treatment of the calculus of variations in terms of differential forms.

2. THE LAGRANGIAN AND CONSTRAINTS

Choose indices $0 \leq \mu,\nu \leq 3$. Let $g_{\mu\nu}$ be the Lorentz metric tensor, x^μ space-time coordinates.

$$(g^{\mu\nu}) = \text{inverse of } (g_{\mu\nu}) \quad .$$

Let X be the space whose variables are labeled

$$F_{\mu\nu},\ A_\mu,\ x^\mu \quad ,$$

with

$$F_{\mu\nu} = -F_{\nu\mu}$$

(Note that $F_{\mu\nu}, A_\mu$ are *independent* variables. They are the coordinates of a vector bundle over R^4.) Set:

$$dx = dx^0 \wedge \cdots \wedge dx^3$$

Set:

$$F^{\mu\nu} = g^{\mu\mu'} g^{\nu\nu'} F_{\mu'\nu'} \tag{2.1}$$

$$L = F^{\mu\nu} F_{\mu\nu} \tag{2.2}$$

$$\theta = F_{\mu\nu}dx^{\mu} \wedge dx^{\nu} - d(A_{\mu}dx^{\mu}) \quad . \tag{2.3}$$

The usual variational principle for Maxwell is to extremize

$$\int L\, dx \quad , \tag{2.4}$$

subject to the constant

$$\theta = 0 \quad .$$

3. THE MAGIC FORMULA FOR THE EXTREMALS

Keep the notation of Section 2. We can handle this in accordance with a general procedure described in Volumes 16 and 17 of IM, namely set

$$\Omega = Ldx + \theta \wedge \lambda \tag{3.1}$$

λ is a two-form we are free to choose, and Ω is a four-form on X. Let us try to find a form η such that *with suitable choice* λ,

$$d\Omega = \theta \wedge \eta \quad . \tag{3.2}$$

In accordance with the general procedure, the *extremals* will be solution submanifolds of the following exterior differential system

$$\eta = 0 = \theta \tag{3.3}$$

$$\begin{aligned} d\Omega &= dL \wedge dx + d\theta \wedge \lambda + \theta \wedge d\lambda \\ &= dL \wedge dx + dF \wedge \lambda + (F - dA) \wedge d\lambda \end{aligned} \tag{3.4}$$

with

$$F = F_{\mu\nu}dx^{\mu}dx^{\nu} \tag{3.5}$$

$$A = A_{\mu}dx^{\mu} \tag{3.6}$$

Also,

$$\theta \wedge \eta = (F - dA) \wedge \eta \quad . \tag{3.7}$$

Notice that the terms involving $dF_{\mu\nu}$ do not appear on the right hand side of (3.7). This suggests that we choose λ so as to eliminate these terms from the right hand side of (3.4). Now,

$$dL = dF^{\mu\nu}F_{\mu\nu} + F^{\mu\nu}dF_{\mu\nu}$$

$$= g^{\mu\mu'}g^{\nu\nu'}(dF_{\mu'\nu'}F_{\mu\nu} + F_{\mu'\nu'}dF_{\mu\nu})$$

$$= 2g^{\mu\mu'}g^{\nu\nu'}F_{\mu'\nu'}dF_{\mu\nu}$$

$$= 2F^{\mu\nu}dF_{\mu\nu} \qquad (3.8)$$

$$dL \wedge dx + dF \wedge \lambda = 2F^{\mu\nu}dF_{\mu\nu} \wedge dx + dF_{\mu\nu} \wedge dx^{\mu} \wedge dx^{\nu} \wedge \lambda \qquad (3.9)$$

Let us try to make the right hand side of (3.9) vanish with a choice for λ of the following form:

$$\lambda = \lambda_{\mu\nu}dx^{\mu} \wedge dx^{\nu} \qquad (3.10)$$

and

$$2F^{\mu\nu}dx = dx^{\mu} \wedge dx^{\nu} \wedge \lambda \qquad (3.11)$$

We recognize that:

$$\lambda = *F \quad , \qquad (3.12)$$

where $*F$ is the *Hodge dual* of the two-form F. (In fact, this can be taken as the *definition* of $*F$.)

Let us now put this value for λ back into (3.4)

$$\boxed{d\Omega = \theta \wedge d(*F)} \qquad (3.13)$$

Thus, we see that we have proved:

Theorem 3.1. The extremals of this variational problem

$$\int L \, dx \quad ,$$

are the four dimensional solution submanifolds on which $dx \neq 0$, of the exterior differential system generated by

$$F - dA, \ d(*F) \qquad (3.14)$$

or, alternately, by

$$dF, \ d(*F) \quad . \tag{3.15}$$

These are the Maxwell equations in their usual "relativistic" form.

4. THE YANG-MILLS GENERALIZATION

Introduce the space of variables

$$(x^{\mu}, A^{a}_{\mu}, F^{a}_{\mu\nu}) \quad , \qquad 1 \le a,b \le m \; ; \quad 0 \le \mu,\nu \le 3 \quad .$$

$$dx = dx^{0} \wedge \cdots \wedge dx^{3} \quad . \tag{4.1}$$

$$\theta^{a} = F^{a}_{\mu\nu} dx^{\mu} \wedge dx^{\nu} - d(A^{a}_{\mu} dx^{\mu}) - C^{a}_{bc} A^{b}_{\mu} A^{c}_{\nu} dx^{\mu} \wedge dx^{\nu} \tag{4.2}$$

(C^{a}_{bc}) are the structure constants of a compact Lie algebra $\mathcal{G}$ (i.e., they are completely skew-symmetric in the indices).

$$F^{\mu\nu}_{a} = g^{\mu\mu'} g^{\nu\nu'} \delta_{ab} F^{b}_{\mu'\nu'} \tag{4.3}$$

$$L = F^{\mu\nu}_{a} F^{a}_{\mu\nu} \tag{4.4}$$

Set:

$$\Omega = L dx + \theta^{a} \wedge \lambda_{a} \quad , \tag{4.5}$$

where (λ_{a}) is a set of two-forms. Thus,

$$d\Omega = dL \wedge dx + d\theta^{a} \wedge \lambda_{a} + \theta^{a} \wedge d\lambda_{a} \quad . \tag{4.6}$$

Again, we *impose* the condition that

$$d\Omega = \theta^{a} \wedge \eta_{a} \quad , \tag{4.7}$$

where η_{a} is a set of 3 forms. The extremals are then *defined* as the four-dimensional solution submanifolds (on which $dx \neq 0$) of the exterior differential system

$$\theta^{a} = 0 = \eta_{a} \tag{4.8}$$

In order to calculate λ_{a} and η_{a}, proceed as follows. Set:

$$F^{a} = F^{a}_{\mu\nu} dx^{\mu} \wedge dx^{\nu} \tag{4.9}$$

$$A^a = A^a_\mu dx^\mu \quad . \tag{4.10}$$

Using these forms (4.2) can be shortened to

$$\theta^a = F^a - dA^a - C^a_{bc} A^b \wedge A^c \quad . \tag{4.11}$$

Hence,

$$d\theta^a = dF^a - 2C^a_{bc} dA^b \wedge A^c$$

$$= dF^a - 2C^a_{bc}(\theta^b + C^b_{b'c'} A^{b'} \wedge A^{c'} - F^b) \wedge A^c$$

$= \text{, using the Jacobi identities for the } C^a_{bc} \text{ ,}$

$$dF^a - 2C^a_{bc}(\theta^b - F^b) \wedge A^c \quad . \tag{4.12}$$

((4.12) is essentially what differential geometers call the *Bianchi identity*.)

Insert (4.12) into (4.6):

$$d\Omega = dL \wedge dx + (dF^a - 2C^a_{bc}(\theta^b - F^b) \wedge A^c) \wedge \lambda_a + \theta^a \wedge d\lambda_a \tag{4.13}$$

Impose (4.7) by the following Ansatz:

$$dL \wedge dx + dF^a \wedge \lambda_a + 2C^a_{bc} F^b \wedge A^c \wedge \lambda_a = 0 \quad . \tag{4.14}$$

η_a is then given by the following formula:

$$\eta_a = d\lambda_a - 2C^b_{ca} A^c \wedge \lambda_b \quad . \tag{4.15}$$

Bibliography

1. F.B. Estabrook and B.K. Harrison, "Geometric Approach to Invariance Groups and Solution of Partial Differential Systems", J. Math. Phys. 12 (1971), 653-666.

Appendix E

SIMILARITY SOLUTIONS OF DIFFERENTIAL EQUATIONS DEFINED BY SYMMETRY GROUPS

By Frank Estabrook, Robert Hermann, and Hugo Wahlquist

1. INTRODUCTION

One important application of Lie group theory is in generating special solutions of differential equations on which they act as symmetries. While this goes back to Lie, only recently has it been thought about systematically [1]. In this work we briefly describe a general method for constructing special solutions based on Cartan's theory of exterior differential systems.

2. EXTERIOR DIFFERENTIAL SYSTEMS AND THEIR INFINITESIMAL SYMMETRIES ("ISOVECTORS")

Let X be a manifold. An *exterior differential system*, E, is a collection of differential forms which is closed under the operation of exterior multiplication by an arbitrary differential form on X.

An *integral manifold* (≡ *solution manifold*) of E is a map

$$\phi : Y \to X$$

such that:

a) ϕ is a submanifold map, i.e., $\phi_* : T(Y) \to T(X)$ is one-one

b) $\phi^*(\theta) = 0$ for all $\theta \in E$.

A vector field V on X is an *infinitesimal symmetry* ("isovector", in the terminology of [1]) if

$$\mathscr{L}_V(\theta) \in E \tag{2.1}$$

for all $\theta \in E$.

($\mathscr{L}$ ≡ Lie derivative operation.) In view of the fundamental identity

$$\mathscr{L}_V(\theta) = d(V \lrcorner\, \theta) + V \lrcorner\, d\theta \tag{2.2}$$

condition (2.1) can be written as:

$$d(V \lrcorner\, \theta) + V \lrcorner\, d\theta \in E \tag{2.3}$$

for all $\theta \in E$.

This condition implies that the one-parameter group $t \to \exp(tV)$ of diffeomorphisms of X generated by V leaves invariant E, and *also* maps an integral manifold into an integral manifold. Thus, V generates a one-parameter group of *symmetries* of the underlying differential equations.

3. CAUCHY CHARACTERISTICS

Let E be an exterior differential system on a manifold X. A vector field $V \in \mathcal{V}(X)$ is *Cauchy characteristic* if

$$V \lrcorner \theta \in E \tag{3.1}$$

for all $\theta \in E$.

It follows from (2.3) (and the condition that $dE \subset E$) that V is *also* an infinitesimal symmetry (but not necessarily vice-versa).

<u>Theorem 3.1</u>. Let $\mathcal{C}$ denote the set of all Cauchy characteristic vector fields of the exterior differential system E. Then,

a) $[\mathcal{C},\mathcal{C}] \subset \mathcal{C}$ (3.2)

b) $[V,\mathcal{C}] \subset \mathcal{C}$ if V is an infinitesimal symmetry

c) Suppose that $\pi: X \to Z$ is a submersion map whose fibers are all tangent to $\mathcal{C}$. Then, there is an exterior differential system E' on Z such that:

$$\boxed{E = \text{system on } X \text{ generated by } \pi^*(E')\ .} \tag{3.3}$$

If $\phi: Y \to Z$ is an integral submanifold of E', set

$$Y' = \pi^{-1}(\phi(Y)) \quad .$$

The inclusion map $Y' \to X$ is then an integral submanifold of E. Thus, an integral submanifold of dimension m of E' generates an integral submanifold of dimension $m + m'$ of E. (m = dimension of the fiber of π.)

These results are well-known in the theory of exterior differential systems.

4. SIMILARITY SOLUTIONS OF EXTERIOR DIFFERENTIAL SYSTEMS

Let E be an exterior differential system on a manifold X. Let G be a Lie transformation group on X. Let $\mathcal{G}$ be the Lie algebra of G, considered as a Lie algebra of vector fields on X. Suppose that G *leaves* E *invariant*, i.e.,

$$g^*(E) = E \tag{4.1}$$

for all $g \in G$.

It then follows that $\mathcal{G}$ is a Lie algebra of infinitesimal symmetries of E.

Now, suppose that E' is another exterior differential system on X with

$$E \subset E' \tag{4.2}$$

Then,

> All integral manifolds of E' are also integral submanifolds of E, i.e., the solution of the differential equations corresponding to E' are *special solutions* of the differential equations corresponding to E.

Let us suppose also that the orbit space

$$G\backslash X \equiv Z \tag{4.3}$$

is a manifold, and that the projection map

$$X \to G\backslash X \equiv Z$$

(which assigns to each $x \in X$ the orbit Gx on which it lies) is a *submersion.* (Then, all orbits have the same dimension, and the possible singularities of the action of G have already been taken out of X.)

Definition. E' satisfying (4.2) defines a set of *similarity solutions* of E, relative to G, if the vector fields in $\mathcal{G}$ are *Cauchy characteristic* for E'.

Given such an E', the construction of the special solution of E proceeds as follows. By the Cauchy characteristic theorem quoted in the previous section, there is an exterior system E" on $G\backslash X$ such that:

$$\pi^*(E") \text{ generates } E' \quad ,$$

where $\pi: G \to G\backslash X$ is the map

$$x \to (\text{orbit } Gx) \quad .$$

Let

$$S \subset G\backslash X$$

be an integral submanifold of E''. Then,

$$\pi^{-1}(S)$$

is the *similarity solution of* E *generated by* S *and* G.

We have now completed the explanation of the generalities. Let us proceed to study the special cases.

5. SIMILARITY SOLUTIONS WITH RESPECT TO A ONE-PARAMETER GROUP OF SYMMETRIES

Let E be an exterior differential system on the manifold X with $V \in \mathcal{V}(X)$ a vector field such that

$$\mathcal{L}_V(E) \subset E \quad . \tag{5.1}$$

Set:

$$\boxed{E' = \text{exterior system generated by } E, \text{ and the forms } V \lrcorner \theta, \text{ with } \theta \in E .} \tag{5.2}$$

Now,

$$d(V \lrcorner \theta) = \mathcal{L}_V(\theta) - V \lrcorner d\theta \quad . \tag{5.3}$$

Since (by (5.1) and the fact that $dE \subset E$) the right hand side of (5.3) *automatically* belongs to E', we see that it is not necessary to add the exterior derivatives of $V \lrcorner E$.

Note that

$$V \lrcorner E' \subset E' \quad , \tag{5.4}$$

i.e.,

$$V \textit{ is Cauchy characteristic for } E' . \tag{5.5}$$

Hence, there is a manifold Z, a map

$$\pi: X \to Z$$

whose fibers are the orbits of V (in the region where V is nonzero) and an exterior system E'' on Z such that

$$E' \text{ is generated by } \pi^*(E") \quad . \tag{5.6}$$

This general method is basically what Lie would have done to "reduce the order of the system". Choose local coordinates (x^i), $1 \le i,j \le n$, for X so that

$$V = \frac{\partial}{\partial x^1} \quad .$$

The $(x^2,\dots,x^n)$ are the pull-backs of a coordinate system on Z. $E"$ is a system in the variables

$$(x^2,\dots,x^n) \quad .$$

Thus, *the symmetry has been used to reduce the number of variables of the system.*

6. SIMILARITY SOLUTIONS FOR A LIE ALGEBRA OF SYMMETRIES

Let E be an exterior differential system on a manifold X. Let $\mathcal{G}$ be a Lie algebra of vector fields on X such that:

$$\mathcal{L}_V(E) \subset E \tag{6.1}$$

$$\text{for all } V \in \mathcal{V}(X) \quad .$$

Let

$$\boxed{\begin{array}{l} E' = \text{exterior system generated by } E \text{ and the forms} \\ \qquad V_1 \lrcorner \theta \\ \qquad V_1 \lrcorner V_2 \lrcorner \theta \\ \qquad \vdots \end{array}} \tag{6.2}$$

where $\theta \in E$; $V_1, V_2, \dots \in \mathcal{G}$. Now

$$d(V_1 \lrcorner \theta) = \mathcal{L}_{V_1}(\theta) - V_1 \lrcorner d\theta$$

$$\begin{aligned} d(V_1 \lrcorner V_2 \lrcorner \theta) &= \mathcal{L}_{V_1}(V_2 \lrcorner \theta) - V_1 \lrcorner d(V_2 \lrcorner \theta) \\ &= [V_1,V_2] \lrcorner \theta + V_2 \lrcorner \mathcal{L}_{V_1}(\theta) - V_1 \lrcorner d(V_2 \lrcorner \theta) \quad . \end{aligned}$$

These identities (and those that follow by induction) show that *it is not necessary to add the exterior derivatives* of the forms in (6.2). Further,

$$\text{$\mathcal{G}$ \textit{is a Lie algebra of Cauchy characteristic vector fields of} } E' . \tag{6.3}$$

Hence, there is (locally, in the neighborhood of the regular points of $\mathcal{G}$) a fiber space

$$\pi : X \to Z$$

and an exterior system E'' on Z such that

The fibers of π are the orbits of $\mathcal{G}$

$\pi^*(E'')$ generates E' .

In particular, if $S \subset Z$ is an integral submanifold of E'', then

$$\pi^{-1}(S)$$

is an integral submanifold of E' *and* E. It is a *similarity solution.*

Let us now turn to working out the simplest interesting example.

7. THE THREE-DIMENSIONAL HELMHOLTZ-WAVE EQUATION AND ITS SIMILARITY SOLUTIONS UNDER THE ROTATION GROUP

Introduce indices

$$1 \le i,j \le 3 \quad ,$$

and X the space of variables

$$(x^i, y, p_i, p_{ij}) \quad ,$$

$$p_{ij} = p_{ji} \quad .$$

Let E be the exterior differential system generated by

$$f = \delta^{ij} p_{ij} - \lambda y$$

$$\theta = dy = p_i dx^i \tag{7.1}$$

$$\theta_i = dp_i - p_{ij} dx^j \quad .$$

The three-dimensional integral submanifolds on which

$$dx^1 \wedge dx^2 \wedge dx^3 \neq 0$$

are then in correspondence with the functions $y(x)$ such that

$$\delta^{ij} \frac{\partial^2 y}{\partial x^i \partial x^j} = \lambda y \quad . \tag{7.2}$$

(7.2) is the Helmholtz-wave equation, which plays the basic role in classical mathematical physics.

Let $\mathcal{G}$ be the Lie algebra of vector fields in the variables (x^i) spanned by those of the form

$$V^i = \varepsilon_j^{ik} x^j \frac{\partial}{\partial x^k} \quad . \tag{7.3}$$

V^i generate the *rotation group* acting on R^3. ($\varepsilon_j^{ik} \equiv \varepsilon_{ijk}$ is the completed skew-symmetric tensor.)

Extend the action to X via *prolongation.*

$$\boxed{V^i(y) = 0}$$

$$\mathcal{L}_{V^i}(\theta) = V^i(p_j)dx^j - p_j dV^i(x^j)$$

$$= V^i(p_j)dx^j - p_j \varepsilon_k^{ij} dx^k \quad .$$

Set:

$$\boxed{V^i(p_j) = p_k \varepsilon_j^{ik}} \tag{7.4}$$

With this choice,

$$\mathcal{L}_{V^i}(\theta) = 0 \quad .$$

Similarly, let V^i act on the p_{ij} so that $\mathcal{L}_{V^i}(\theta_j) = 0$. (This is what is meant by "prolongation".)

$$\mathcal{L}_{V^i}(\theta_j) = dV^i(p_j) - V^i(p_{jk})dx^k - p_{jk}dV^i(x^k)$$

$$= \varepsilon_j^{ik}dp_k - V^i(p_{jk})dx^k - p_{jk}\varepsilon_\ell^{ik}dx^\ell$$

$$= \varepsilon_j^{ik}\theta_k + \varepsilon_j^{ik}p_{k\ell}dx^\ell - V^i(p_{jk})dx^j - p_{jk}\varepsilon_\ell^{ik}dx^\ell$$

or

$$\boxed{V^i(p_{jk}) = p_{j\ell}\varepsilon_k^{i\ell} - p_{\ell k}\varepsilon_j^{i\ell}} \tag{7.5}$$

In order to construct similarity solutions following the method of Section 6, we must add to E the forms resulting from contraction with the vector fields V^i.

$$V^i \lrcorner\, df = V^i(f)$$

$$= \delta^{jk}V^i(p_{jk})$$

$$= \delta^{jk}(p_{j\ell}\varepsilon_k^{i\ell} - p_{\ell k}\varepsilon_j^{i\ell})$$

$$= p_{k\ell}\varepsilon_k^{i\ell} - p_{\ell k}\varepsilon_k^{i\ell}$$

$$= \boxed{0} \tag{7.6}$$

$$V^i \lrcorner\, \theta = -p_jV^i(x^j)$$

$$= \boxed{-p_j\varepsilon_k^{ij}x^k} \tag{7.7}$$

$$V^i \lrcorner\, \theta_j = V^i(p_j) - p_{jk}\varepsilon_\ell^{ik}x^\ell$$

$$= \boxed{p_k \varepsilon_j^{ik} - p_{jk} \varepsilon_\ell^{ik} x^\ell} \tag{7.8}$$

$$V^i \lrcorner\, d\theta = \mathscr{L}_{V^i}(\theta) - d(V^i \lrcorner\, \theta) \tag{7.9}$$

$$V^i \lrcorner\, d\theta_j = \mathscr{L}_{V^i}(\theta_j) - d(V^i \lrcorner\, \theta_j) \tag{7.10}$$

Since V^i has been chosen so that the Lie derivatives of θ, θ_i are zero, we can ignore (7.9) and (7.10) in generating E'. Thus, to generate E', we have only to add to E the functions on the right hand side of (7.7) and (7.8), plus their exterior derivatives.

We can now see immediately what the three-dimensional integral manifolds of E' are. Since (assuming $dx^1 \wedge dx^2 \wedge dx^3 \neq 0$) they are of the form

$$x \to y(x), \; p_i = \frac{\partial y}{\partial x^i}, \; p_{ij} = \frac{\partial^2 y}{\partial x^i x^j}$$

$$V^i \lrcorner\, \theta = 0$$

means that

$$\frac{\partial y}{\partial x^j} \varepsilon_k^{ij} x^k = 0 \quad ,$$

or, in classical vector analysis notation,

$$(\nabla y) \times \vec{x} = 0 \tag{7.11}$$

This means that

$$\boxed{y(x) \text{ is a function of } r = \sqrt{\delta_{ij} x^i x^j} \text{ alone}} \tag{7.12}$$

The integral manifolds of E' are then determined as the *solutions of the Helmholtz equations which are functions of* r *alone*, i.e., which are *invariant under the action of the rotation group.*

We can see what is going on very easily in terms of the theory of *Ehresmann jets.* E lives on the space

$$J^2(R^3,R) \quad ,$$

two-jets of mappings $R^3 \to R$. $G = SO(3,R)$ acts on $J^2(R^3,R)$, leaving E invariant. Consider maps

$$\phi: R^3 \to R$$

which are *invariant* under G, i.e.,

$$\phi(gx) = \phi(x) \tag{7.13}$$

$$\text{for all } x \in R^3, \quad g \in G \quad .$$

Let

$$\pi: J^2(R^3,R) \to G\backslash J^2(R^3,R)$$

be the projection onto the orbit space. Then, the maps

$$x \to \pi j^2(\phi)(x) \quad ,$$

for ϕ a solution of the Helmholtz equation satisfying (7.13), i.e., which are rotationally symmetric, are the integral submanifolds of the exterior system E".

Of course, this result holds a good deal more generally than this one example. We see that:

> The equations of mathematical physics correspond to exterior differential systems on $J^2(R^4,R^m)$. They admit symmetry groups G, which are transformation groups on $J^2(R^4,R^m)$. Their "similarity solutions" correspond to exterior differential systems on the orbit spaces
>
> $$G\backslash J^2(R^4,R^m) \quad .$$

Much of the calculational work in any treatise (or research paper) in mathematical or theoretical physics then involves a specific choice of G and coordinates for the orbit space and E". It would be enormously useful to have unified methods of doing these calculations!

8. SIMILARITY SOLUTIONS OF THE MAXWELL EQUATIONS

In [1] the Maxwell equations were written in a convenient form as an exterior differential system. We will now use this form to look for similarity solutions.

Let X be the space of variables

$$(x^i, t, E_i, B_i) \quad , \qquad 1 \le i,j \le 3 \quad .$$

$$\omega = E_i dx^i \wedge dt + \frac{1}{C} \varepsilon^i_{jk} B_i dx^j \wedge dx^k \tag{8.1}$$

$$\omega' = B_i dx^i \wedge dt - \frac{1}{C} \varepsilon^i_{jk} E_i dx^j \wedge dx^k \tag{8.2}$$

$$M = \text{exterior differential system generated by } d\omega \text{ and } d\omega'$$

(M stands for *Maxwell*.) Let

$$(x^1, x^2, x^3, t) \rightarrow E_i(\vec{x}, t),\ B_i(\vec{x}, t)$$

$$= \vec{E}(\vec{x}, t),\ B(\vec{x}, t)$$

be an integral manifold of M parameterized by $(\vec{x}, t)$, i.e., such that

$$dx^1 \wedge dx^2 \wedge dx^3 \wedge dt$$

is nonzero. Thus we see that the integral manifold conditions are:

$$\begin{aligned} \text{curl } \vec{E} &= -\frac{1}{C}\frac{\partial \vec{B}}{\partial t} \\ \text{div } \vec{B} &= 0 \\ \text{curl } \vec{B} &= \frac{1}{C}\frac{\partial \vec{E}}{\partial t} \\ \text{div } \vec{E} &= 0 \end{aligned} \tag{8.3}$$

These are the *free Maxwell equations*.

Introduce the three vector fields V^i which generate the rotation group:

$$V^i(x^j) = \varepsilon^{ij}_k x^k \tag{8.4a}$$

$$\mathscr{L}_{V^i}(E_j dx^j) = 0 = \mathscr{L}_{V^i}(B_j dx^j) \tag{8.4b}$$

Thus,

$$\mathscr{L}_{V^i}(\omega) = 0 = \mathscr{L}_{V^i}(\omega') \tag{8.5}$$

$$V^i \lrcorner\, d\omega = -\, d(V^i \lrcorner\, \omega) \tag{8.6}$$

$$V^i \lrcorner\, d\omega' = -\, d(V^i \lrcorner\, \omega') \tag{8.7}$$

$$\begin{aligned} V^j \lrcorner\, (V^i \lrcorner\, d\omega) &= -\, V^j \lrcorner\, d(V^i \lrcorner\, \omega) \\ &= -\, \mathscr{L}_{V^j}(V^i \lrcorner\, \omega) + d(V^j \lrcorner\, V^i \lrcorner\, \omega) \\ &= [V^i, V^j] \lrcorner\, \omega + d(V^j \lrcorner\, V^i \lrcorner\ \ ) \end{aligned} \tag{8.8}$$

Thus, the similarity solutions are defined by the additional relations:

$$\begin{aligned} V^i \lrcorner\, \omega &= 0 = V^i \lrcorner\, \omega' \\ \omega(V^i, V^j) &= 0 = \omega'(V^i, V^j) \end{aligned} \tag{8.9}$$

Now,

$$V^i \lrcorner\, \omega = E_i V(x^i)\, dt + 2\, \frac{1}{C}\, \varepsilon^i_{jk} B_i V(x^j)\, dx^k$$

$$V \lrcorner\, \omega' = B_i V(x^i)\, dt - \frac{1}{C}\, 2\varepsilon^i_{jk} E_i V(x^j)\, dx^k$$

The relations (8.9) then are equivalent to the following

$$\begin{aligned} E_i &= f x^i \\ B_i &= g x^i \end{aligned} \tag{8.10}$$

for some functions f and g. Requiring that these relations pass to quotient to live on $G\backslash X$ gives:

$$f, g \text{ are functions of } (r,t) \text{ alone.} \tag{8.11}$$

Thus, we obtain the following not unexpected result.

Theorem 8.1. The similarity solutions

$$E = E_i dx^i , \qquad B = B_i dx^i$$

of Maxwell's equations (relative to the rotation group) are those which are, *as differential forms*, invariant under the rotation group, i.e., which satisfy

$$\mathscr{L}_{V^i}(E) = 0 = \mathscr{L}_{V^i}(B) \tag{8.12}$$

where V^1, V^2, V^3 are the vector fields generating the rotation group.

This result can now be sharpened as follows.

Theorem 8.2. Any pair E, B of time-dependent forms on R^3 which satisfy (8.12) *plus* Maxwell's equation, is actually time-independent, i.e., also satisfies

$$\frac{\partial E}{\partial t} = \frac{\partial B}{\partial t} = 0 \tag{8.13}$$

Proof. This follows readily from Maxwell's equation (8.3).

The corresponding result in general relativity--rotational invariance implies stationarity--is called *Birkhoff's theorem*.

Bibliogrpahy

1. F.B. Estabrook and B.K. Harrison, "Geometric Approach to Invariance Groups and Solution of Partial Differential Systems", J. Math. Phys. 12 (1971), 653-666.

Appendix F

GENERAL FIELD THEORIES DESCRIBED BY MEANS OF DIFFERENTIAL FORMS. FIELD THEORETIC SYMPLECTIC STRUCTURES INSTANTONS AND SOLITONS

1. INTRODUCTION

In my previous books (beginning with *Lie Algebras and Quantum Mechanics*) I have gradually perfected the study of the multiple integral calculus of variations by means of higher-degree differential forms, as classical, one independent variable calculus of variations, Hamilton-Jacobi is described in terms of two-forms, i.e., the theory of symplectic manifolds. I believe that ultimately one will want to develop a good deal of classical and quantum field theory in terms of a "pure" theory of such forms. In this appendix I will develop this theory further, then go on to briefly indicate how it can be used to study the currently fashionable topics of elementary particle physics. I begin with the description of Yang-Mills in terms of differential forms.

2. THE DIFFERENTIAL FORM FORMALISM FOR YANG-MILLS

Introduce the space X of variables (x, A^a, F^a)

$$1 \leq a,b \leq m \quad , \qquad 0 \leq \mu,\nu \leq 3$$

$$dx = dx^0 \wedge \cdots \wedge dx^3$$

$$\theta^a = F^a_{\mu\nu} dx^\mu \wedge dx^\nu - dA^a_\mu \wedge dx^\mu - C^a_{bc} A^b_\mu A^c_\nu dx^\mu \wedge dx^\nu \quad .$$

(C^a_{bc}) are the structure constants of a compact Lie algebra $\mathcal{G}$ (i.e., they are completely skew-symmetric on their indices.) Set:

$$F^{\mu\nu}_a = g^{\mu\mu'} g^{\nu\nu'} \delta_{ab} F^b_{\mu'\nu'}$$

$(g^{\mu\nu}$ is the inverse of the Lortentz metric tensor.)

$$L = F^{\mu\nu}_a F^a_{\mu\nu} \tag{2.1}$$

$$\omega = L dx + \theta^a \wedge \lambda_a \quad , \tag{2.2}$$

where λ_a is a set of two-forms in the dx^μ (with coefficients depending on

A,F) such that:

$$d\omega \equiv \Omega = \theta^a \wedge d\lambda_a \tag{2.3}$$

The equations of the Yang-Mills themselves are

$$\theta^a = 0 = d\lambda_a \quad , \tag{2.4}$$

i.e., (2.2) defines an exterior differential system on X whose four-dimensional integral manifolds on which $dx \neq 0$ are determined as functions

$$A^a_\mu(x) , F^a_{\mu\nu}(x) \quad .$$

The forms λ_a are readily calculated from (2.2)

$$d\omega = dL \wedge dx + d\theta^a \wedge \lambda_a + \theta^a \wedge d\lambda_a \quad ,$$

hence

$$dL \wedge dx + d\theta^a \wedge \lambda_a = 0 \tag{2.5}$$

3. INFINITESIMAL SYMMETRIES

A vector field V on X is an *infinitesimal symmetry* if

$$\mathcal{L}_V(\Omega) = 0 \quad . \tag{3.1}$$

A three-form η such that

$$d\eta = - V \lrcorner\, d\Omega \tag{3.2}$$

is then a *conserved current* associated with V. If

$$\phi : R^4 \to X$$

is an integral manifold of (2.5), then the three dimensional integral

$$\int_{(3\text{-D submanifold of } R^4)} \phi^*(\eta) \tag{3.3}$$

is the *charge* associated with the current. (It follows from (2.5) that $\phi^*(d\eta) = 0$, so that, by Stokes' theorem, this integral is dependent only on the homotopy class of the submanifold used to define it.)

If V satisfies the following condition

$$\mathcal{L}_V(\omega) = 0 \tag{3.4}$$

then it obviously also satisfies (3.1), i.e., (3.4) defines a special type of infinitesimal symmetry. For this type,

$$\boxed{\eta = V \lrcorner \omega} \tag{3.5}$$

since then

$$\begin{aligned} d\eta &= d(V \lrcorner \omega) \\ &= \mathcal{L}_V(\omega) - V \lrcorner d\omega \\ &= -V \lrcorner \Omega \end{aligned}$$

We can now use this formula to study the *energy momentum tensor*.

4. THE ENERGY-MOMENTUM TENSOR

Let $\partial_\mu = \partial/\partial x^\mu$. Then, obviously

$$\mathcal{L}_{\partial_\mu}(\omega) = 0 \quad .$$

Set:

$$\eta_\mu = \partial_\mu \lrcorner \omega \tag{4.1}$$

It is a three-form, the *conserved current*

$$\int_{R^3} \phi^*(\eta_0)$$

defines the *energy* of a solution $\phi: R^4 \to X$ of the Yang-Mills equations.

Using (2.2), let us compute η_0, the *energy-density form*.

$$\eta_0 = L d\vec{x} + (\partial_0 \lrcorner \theta^a) \wedge \lambda_a + \theta^a \wedge (\partial_0 \lrcorner \lambda_a) \tag{4.2}$$

Now,

$$\partial_0 \lrcorner \theta^a = 2F^a_{0\mu} dx^\mu + dA^a_0 - 2C^a_{bc} A^b_0 A^c_\mu dx^\mu \tag{4.3}$$

Let us suppose that

$$\lambda_a = \lambda_{a,\mu\nu} dx^\mu \wedge dx^\nu \quad . \tag{4.4}$$

Then,

$$\partial_0 \lrcorner \lambda_a = 2\lambda_{a,0\mu} dx^\mu \tag{4.5}$$

Hence,

$$\eta_0 |_{dx_0 = 0} = L d\vec{x} + 2(F^a_{0i} dx^i + dA^a_0 - 2C^a_{bc} A^b_0 A^c_i dx^i) \wedge \lambda_{a,jk} dx^j \wedge dx^k + \cdots$$

$$\phi^*(\eta_0) |_{dx_0 = 0} = L d\vec{x} + 2(F^a_{0i} - 2C^a_{bc} A^b_0 A^c_i) \varepsilon^{ijk} \lambda_{a,jk} d\vec{x} + \varepsilon^{ijk} \partial_i (A^a_0) \lambda_{a,jk} d\vec{x} \tag{4.6}$$

The expression of the right hand side is the *energy-density* of the Yang-Mills field. This can be readily simplified to the form found in the physics literature, but I will not go into that here.

5. A GENERAL FIELD THEORY DESCRIBED BY DIFFERENTIAL FORMS

Let X be a manifold. (In the physical examples it will be a suitable jet fiber bundle over space-time.) Let m be an integer. (In relativistic physics, it is four, the dimension of the base space of the bundle.) Let

$$\Omega$$

be a *closed* $(m+1)$-differential form on X.

Definition. A *prolongation* is a set (η_a, θ^a), $1 \le a,b \le n$, of differential forms on X such that

$$\Omega = \eta_a \wedge \theta^a \quad . \tag{5.1}$$

Of course, (5.1) implies that

$$\text{degree } \eta_a + \text{degree } \theta^a = (m+1) \quad . \tag{5.2}$$

However, the *degree of the form* θ^a *may vary with* a.

Let E now denote the *exterior differential system generated by the forms* θ^a, η_a. (Thus, E is the smallest set of forms on X which is closed under exterior differentiation and exterior multiplication by arbitrary forms on X.) E *defines a field theory*. Let Y be an m-dimensional manifold.

$$\mathscr{S}(Y,E)$$

denotes the set of all submanifold maps

$$\phi: Y \to X$$

such that

$$\phi^*(E) = 0 \quad ,$$

i.e., the *integral* or *solution* submanifolds. The elements of $\mathscr{S}(Y,E)$ are the (classical) *states* of the field theory.

6. THE TANGENT SPACE TO THE SPACE OF STATES. THE SYMPLECTIC STRUCTURE

Let $t \to \phi_t$ be a one-parameter family of elements of $\mathscr{S}(Y,E)$, reducing to ϕ at $t = 0$. Let

$$\underline{v}: Y \to T(X)$$

be the *infinitesimal deformation on vector fields* defined as follows

$$\underline{v}(y) = \text{tangent vector to the curve } t \to \phi_t(y) \text{ at } t = 0 \ .$$

For $\theta \in E$, we have:

$$0 = \frac{\partial}{\partial t}\phi_t^*(\theta)\Big|_{t=0}$$

$$= \phi^*(\underline{v} \lrcorner d\theta) + d(\phi^*\underline{v} \lrcorner \theta) \tag{6.1}$$

The set of all such vector fields is the *tangent* space to $\mathscr{S}(Y,E)$ at ϕ, denoted as

$$\mathscr{S}(Y,E)_\phi \quad . \tag{6.2}$$

We can now use Ω to define a skew-symmetric, real-valued bilinear form on each tangent space $\mathscr{S}(Y,E)_\phi$.

Let Z be an (m-1)-dimensional submanifold of X. For $\underline{v}_1, \underline{v}_2 \in \mathscr{S}(Y,E)_\phi$, let

$$\underline{\Omega}(\underline{v}_1,\underline{v}_2) = \int_Z \phi^*(\underline{v}_1 \lrcorner \underline{v}_2 \lrcorner \Omega) \quad . \tag{6.3}$$

As ϕ varies, this defines ("formally", i.e., without worrying about convergence of the integral) a "two-differential form" on the "infinite dimensional manifold $\mathscr{S}(Y,E)$". We will call this a *symplectic structure*. (In fact, it is not strictly so, since it typically will have degeneracies, i.e., Cauchy characteristic vectors.)

7. THE GENERALIZED POISSON BRACKET STRUCTURE

A *conserved current-infinitesimal symmetry* is a pair

$$(\alpha,V)$$

consisting of an (m-1)-form $\alpha \in \mathscr{D}^{m-1}(X)$ and a vector field $V \in \mathscr{V}(X)$ such that

$$d\alpha = - V \lrcorner \Omega \tag{7.1}$$

Remark. It follows from the condition "$d\Omega = 0$" and (7.1) that

$$\begin{aligned} \mathscr{L}_V(\Omega) &= d(V \lrcorner \Omega) + V \lrcorner d\Omega \\ &= - dd\alpha \\ &= 0 \end{aligned} \tag{7.2}$$

i.e., V is an infinitesimal symmetry of the form Ω. Also, from the prolongation formula (5.1), it follows that

$$d\alpha \in E \quad , \tag{7.3}$$

i.e., α is a *conservation law* for the exterior differential system E.

Let $\mathscr{P}(\Omega)$ denote the set of pairs (α,V) satisfying (7.1). ("$\mathscr{P}$" stands for "Poisson".) If (α_1,V_1) and $(\alpha_2,V_2) \in \mathscr{P}$, then (in view of (7.2)),

$$\begin{aligned} [V_1,V_2] \lrcorner \Omega &= \mathscr{L}_{V_1}(V_2 \lrcorner \Omega) \\ &= - \mathscr{L}_{V_1}(d\alpha_2) \\ &= - d\mathscr{L}_{V_1}(\alpha_a) \quad . \end{aligned} \tag{7.4}$$

This suggests that we set

$$[(\alpha_1,V_1),(\alpha_2,V_2)] = (\mathscr{L}_{V_1}(\alpha_2),[V_1,V_2]) \tag{7.5}$$

This formula *makes* $\mathcal{P}$ *into a Lie algebra* which (in special cases) the physicists call *current algebras*. This Lie algebra can be represented via a Poisson bracket (relative to the symplectic structure) as *functions* on $\mathcal{S}(Y,E)$: Assign to $(\alpha,V) \in \mathcal{P}$ the map

$$\phi \to \int_Z \phi^*(\alpha) \equiv f_\alpha(\phi) \tag{7.6}$$

Physicists call the right hand side the *total charge* of the "conserved current" (α,V).

Of course, for a quantum theory, there should be the possibility of representation of at least pieces of this Lie algebra by skew-Hermitian operators on a Hilbert space.

8. SOLITONS AND A "SOLVABLE-COMPLETELY INTEGRABLE" STRUCTURE

The original (and probably only reasonable) Kruskal-Zabusky definition of "soliton" goes as follows. Suppose there are a set $(\alpha_0,V_0),(\alpha_1,V_1),\ldots$ of conserved currents which are "in involution", i.e., whose Poisson brackets are zero. We can then also extremize $f_{\alpha_0}: \mathcal{S}(Y,E) \to R$; the extreme points are the "zero soliton solutions". Then extremize f_{α_1}, *holding* f_{α_0} *constant*. The extreme points of $\mathcal{S}(Y,E)$ are *one-solitons*, and so forth.

Physically, "solitons" have certain stability properties, which are probably "enforced" by their nature on terms of conservation laws.

9. THE GROUND STATES

Consider one conserved current

$$(\alpha,V) \in \mathcal{P}$$

singled out and called *energy* (or *energy momentum*). It defines the function

$$f_\alpha(\phi) = \int_Z \phi^*(\alpha) \tag{9.1}$$

on $\mathcal{S}(Y,E)$; $f_\alpha(\phi)$ is the *energy* of the state ϕ. Assume that

$$f_\alpha(\phi) \geq 0 \tag{9.2}$$

for $\theta \in \mathcal{S}(Y,E)$.

The states ϕ with

$$f_\alpha(\phi) = 0 \tag{9.3}$$

are the *ground states*.

In traditional quantum theory models (e.g., the harmonic oscillators) there is a *unique* ground state. When physicists attempted to understand non-linear field theories, they at first tried to carry over this property. However, recently it has been found convenient (for phenomenological purposes in elementary particle physics) to give up this property and replace it with the following one

There is a group G of symmetries acting on $\mathcal{S}(Y,E)$, which acts transitively on the ground state	(9.4)

In the case of "gauge theories" G is the *gauge group*, i.e., an *infinite dimensional Lie group*. We will see this in more detail later on. However, there has still been very little serious mathematical work in the mathematics of "degenerate ground states". I am very dubious that the physicists really understand what goes on here.

Note that the ground states are the *minima* of the *energy*, a "conserved current". Thus, we see that they are a very special sort of "soliton", according to the basic Kruskal-Zabusky definition as the extrema of a set of conserved currents which are "in involution".

10. ENERGY FOR THE ELECTROMAGNETIC AND YANG-MILLS FIELDS

The definition of energy is often a mysterious rite in the physicist's field theories. (This is especially acute in General Relativity, where there is no group of symmetries available.) I have described how certain parts of it may be formalized in differential geometric terms in *Interdisciplinary Mathematics*, Volume 4, and I will carry these results over, changing notation to conform with that we are now using.

Let Y be a manifold. (Think of Y as a space-time manifold.) $\mathcal{D}^r(Y)$ denotes the r-th degree differential forms on Y. Let

$$(V_1,V_2) \to \langle V_1,V_2\rangle$$

be an inner product on vector fields which defines a *Riemannian metric* for Y. This inner product may be extended to $\mathcal{D}^r(Y)$. First, use it to set up an isomorphism between $\mathcal{V}(Y)$ and $\mathcal{D}^1(Y)$. Then extend it to $\mathcal{D}^r(Y)$ via the following rule:

$$\langle\theta_1\wedge\cdots\wedge\theta_r,\theta'_1\wedge\cdots\wedge\theta'_r\rangle = \sum_{(i_1\cdots i_r)} \pm\left\langle\theta_1,\theta_{i_1}\right\rangle\cdots\left\langle\theta_r,\theta_{i_r}\right\rangle \tag{10.1}$$

If V_μ, $0 \leq \mu,\nu \leq m-1 = \dim Y$ is a basis for $\mathscr{V}(Y)$ such that

$$<V_\mu, V_\nu> = g_{\mu\nu} \tag{10.2}$$

and if θ^μ is the dual basis of $\mathscr{D}^1(Y)$, i.e.,

$$\theta^\mu(V_\nu) = \delta^\mu_\nu \tag{10.3}$$

then it is easily seen that

$$<\theta^\mu, \theta^\nu> = g^{\mu\nu} \tag{10.4}$$

In particular, if

$$g_{\mu\nu} = \begin{cases} 0 & \text{if } \mu \neq \nu \\ \pm 1 & \text{if } \mu = \nu \end{cases} \tag{10.5}$$

i.e., if the basis is *orthonormal*, then $g_{\mu\nu} = g^{\mu\nu}$.

The *volume element form* is that form dy on $\mathscr{D}^m(Y)$ which is *positively oriented* and such that

$$<dy, dy> = \pm 1 \quad .$$

The *Lagrangian* is now the map

$$L\colon \mathscr{D}^1(Y) \to R$$

given by the following formula

$$L(\theta) = \int_Y <d\theta, d\theta> dy \tag{10.6}$$

To define the extreme points of L, calculate

$$\frac{d}{dt} <(\theta + \delta\theta)> \Big|_{t=0} = 2\int_Y <d\delta\theta, d\theta> \ dy \tag{10.7}$$

with $\mathscr{D}^r(Y) \to \mathscr{D}^{m-n}(Y)$ the Hodge-dual operator

$$<\theta_1, \theta_2> dy = \theta_1 \wedge *\theta_2 \tag{10.8}$$

Then

$$\begin{aligned} <d\delta\theta, d\theta> &= d(\delta\theta) \wedge *d\theta \\ &= d((\delta\theta) \wedge *d\theta) - \delta\theta \wedge d*d\theta \quad . \end{aligned}$$

Hence, the right hand side of (10.7) is

$$2\int_Y \delta\theta \wedge d{*}d\theta \quad = \quad 2 \pm \int_Y \langle\delta\theta, {*}d{*}d\theta\rangle$$

Thus, the *extremal* conditions are

$$\boxed{d{*}d\theta = 0} \tag{10.9}$$

Definition. For fixed $\theta \in \mathscr{D}^1(Y)$, let

$$T\colon \mathscr{V}(Y) \times \mathscr{V}(Y) \to \mathscr{F}(Y) \tag{10.10}$$

$$T(V_1,V_2) \quad = \quad -\langle V_1 \lrcorner\, d\theta,\ V_2 \lrcorner\, d\theta\rangle + \frac{1}{2}\langle V_1,V_2\rangle \langle d\theta,d\theta\rangle \tag{10.11}$$

Then T is the *energy-momentum tensor of the electromagnetic field.*

Remark. This is the "symmetric" energy-momentum tensor (which is not in general unique), defined via the Belinfante-Rosenfeld method, i.e., involving a "deformation" of the metric $\langle\,,\rangle$ as explained in IM, Volume 4.

Here is how "energy" itself is defined. Let Z be a codimension one submanifold of Y. Let V be a vector field which is perpendicular to Z (in the Riemannian sense) and of unit length. Then,

$$\int_Z T(V,V)(V \lrcorner\, dy) \tag{10.12}$$

is the *energy* in the electromagnetic field $d\theta$.

We can now show how this reduces to familiar formulas to be found in all engineering and mechanics books. Let

$$Y \quad = \quad R^4 \quad = \quad \text{Minkowski space} \quad .$$

Coordinates for Y are (t,x^i), $1 \le i,j \le m$.

$$Z \quad = \quad \text{submanifold} \quad t = 0 \quad .$$

$$\langle dx^i,dx^j\rangle \quad = \quad -\ \delta^{ij}$$

$$\langle dx^i,dt\rangle \quad = \quad 0$$

$$\langle dt,dt\rangle \quad = \quad 1 \quad .$$

(The velocity of light is normalized to be one.)

$$V = \frac{\partial}{\partial t}$$

$$d\theta = E_i dx^i \wedge dt + B_{ij} dx^i \wedge dx^j \tag{10.13}$$

$$\begin{aligned}
<d\theta, d\theta> &= E_i E_j <dx^i \wedge dt, dx^j \wedge dt> + B_{ij} B_{k\ell} <dx^i \wedge dx^j, dx^k \wedge dx^\ell> \\
&= - E_i E_j \delta^{ij} + B_{ij} B_{ij} - B_{ij} B_{ji} \\
&= - E_i E^i + 2B_{ij} B^{ij} \\
&= - \vec{E} \cdot \vec{E} + \vec{B} \cdot \vec{B} \quad ,
\end{aligned}$$

which is the traditional expression for the Lagrangian

$$\frac{\partial}{\partial t} \lrcorner \; d\theta = - E_i dx^i$$

$$\left\langle \frac{\partial}{\partial t} \lrcorner \; d\theta, \frac{\partial}{\partial t} \lrcorner \; d\theta \right\rangle = - E_i E^i$$

$$T\left(\frac{\partial}{\partial t}, \frac{\partial}{\partial t}\right) = \frac{1}{2} (\vec{E} \cdot \vec{E} + \vec{B} \cdot \vec{B}) \tag{10.14}$$

which is again the usual Poynting formula for the energy in the electromagnetic field.

11. ZERO ENERGY ("GROUND STATE") ELECTROMAGNETIC FIELDS. "INSTANTONS"

Note that

$$T\left(\frac{\partial}{\partial t}, \frac{\partial}{\partial t}\right) \geq 0$$

(for *real* fields). Hence,

$$(\text{total energy} = 0) \Rightarrow (\vec{E} = 0 = \vec{B} \quad \text{at} \quad t = 0) \quad .$$

The Maxwell field equations (a hyperbolic, involution system) now imply that

$$\vec{E} = 0 = \vec{B}$$

identically. However, if one now allows *complex* valued fields, there is another possibility:

$$\sqrt{-1}\ \vec{B} = \vec{E} \quad ,$$

or

$$2B_{ij} = \sqrt{-1}\ \varepsilon^{k}_{ij} E_k \quad . \tag{11.1}$$

Solutions of Maxwell's equations satisfying (11.1) are called *instantons*. It is readily seen that this means

$$* d\theta = \sqrt{-1}\ d\theta \tag{11.2}$$

where $*$ is the Hodge dual operator for Minkowski space.

12. INSTANTONS AS REAL SOLUTIONS ON EUCLIDEAN R^4

What is the geometric meaning of condition (11.1)? To see this, return to the *differential form* interpretation of the electromagnetic field

$$d\theta = E_i dx^i \wedge dt + B_{ij} dx^i \wedge dx^j \quad . \tag{12.1}$$

Now, consider x^i, t as *complex* variables. Set

$$t = \sqrt{-1}\ \tau \tag{12.2}$$

$$d\theta = \sqrt{-1}\ E_i dx^i \wedge d\tau + B_{ij} dx^i \wedge dx^j \tag{12.3}$$

$$= E'_i dx^i \wedge d\tau + B'_{ij} dx^i \wedge dx^j \tag{12.4}$$

with

$$E'_i = \sqrt{-1}\ E_i \quad ,$$

$$B'_{ij} = B_{ij} \quad .$$

This again has the "real" property, at the expense of solving the change of variable (12.2), which changes the Lorentz metric in R^4 to the *Euclidean* metric. Hence,

> Instantons may be considered as *real* self-dual solutions of the Maxwell equations in *Euclidean* R^4.

The point to this is that the Maxwell equations in Euclidean R^4 are an *elliptic* system of partial differential equations. Further, the Maxwell equations and the self-dual conditions are conformally invariant, hence the equations can be carried over to the *constant curvature* metric on the four-sphere, on which is a *compact* manifold. Now, the theory of elliptic partial differential equations on compact manifolds is the most extensively developed part of the discipline--powerful methods are available, culminating in the *Atiyah-Singer index theorem.*

In fact, in this case--the Maxwell equations, i.e., Yang-Mills with an abelian structure group--the question can be settled with the prototypical theory of this sort, Hodge's theory of harmonic integrals. Since $H^2(S^4,R) = 0$, there are *no* nonzero solutions of the Euclidean Maxwell equations which are everywhere regular on the four-sphere.

Often, we find solutions of the equations in the Euclidean case which are *algebraic*. They can then be "analytically continued" over to Minkowski space. One then typically obtains solutions in terms of the space-time variables (x^μ) which are "algebraic" in these coordinates. It is interesting to note that a major topic in the 19-th century theory of nonlinear partial differential equations was precisely this question of classifying the "algebraic" solutions. Unfortunately, this is a very difficult problem to tackle, in general, and there is not too much available in the way of technique.

13. THE YANG-MILLS GENERALIZATION

Everything done in the previous section for Maxwell can now be carried over to Yang-Mills. Let $\mathscr{L}$ be a real Lie algebra. Let

$$\mathscr{D}^r(Y,\mathscr{L})$$

be the r-th degree differential forms on Y *with values in* $\mathscr{L}$. They can be written in the form

$$\omega = \omega_1 \otimes A_1 + \cdots + \omega_n \otimes A_n \tag{13.1}$$

$$\omega_1,\ldots,\omega_n \in \mathscr{D}^r(Y) \quad ,$$

i.e., *scalar* differential forms

$$A_1,\ldots,A_n \in \mathscr{L} \quad .$$

Suppose given a

$$\theta \in \mathscr{D}^1(Y,\mathscr{L}) \quad .$$

It determines a map

$$\mathscr{D}^r(Y,\mathscr{L}) \to \mathscr{D}^{r+1}(Y,\mathscr{L})$$

called *covariant differentiation.* If

$$\theta = \theta_1 \otimes A_1 + \cdots + \theta_n \otimes A_n \quad ,$$

$$\omega = \omega_1 \otimes B_1 + \cdots + \omega_n \otimes B_n \quad ,$$

then

$$D_\theta(\omega) = d\omega_1 \otimes B_1 + \cdots + d\omega_n \otimes B_n \pm \sum_{i,j=1}^{n} (\theta_i \wedge \omega_j) \otimes [A_i, B_j] \tag{13.2}$$

Suppose also that $\langle\, , \rangle$ is the inner product on differential forms determined by a Riemannian metric on Y and that $\langle\, , \rangle$ is an inner product in $\mathscr{L}$ invariant under the adjoint representation (e.g., the Killing form). One can then define an inner product on $\mathscr{D}^r(Y, \mathscr{L})$ in the usual "tensor product" way:

$$\langle \theta, \omega \rangle = \sum \langle \theta_i, \omega_j \rangle \, (A_i, B_j) \tag{13.3}$$

Similarly, the Hodge dual operator $*$ can be generalized:

$$dy \, \langle \theta, \omega \rangle = \theta \wedge (*\omega) \quad , \tag{13.4}$$

where

$$\theta \wedge \omega = \sum_{i,j} (\theta_i \wedge \omega_j)(A_i, B_j) \tag{13.5}$$

Alternately,

$$*\omega = \sum (*\omega_i) \otimes B_i \quad , \tag{13.6}$$

where $(*\omega_i)$ is the Hodge dual of ω_i as a scalar differential form (with respect to the Riemannian metric on Y) and B_i is an orthonormal basis of $\mathscr{L}$, i.e.,

$$(B_i, B_j) = \delta_{ij} \quad .$$

Exactly the same formulas now hold for Yang-Mills as for Maxwell. The field equations are

$$\begin{aligned} D_\theta \theta &= 0 \\ D_\theta * D_\theta \theta &= 0 \end{aligned} \tag{13.7}$$

(The major difference is that now the "potential" θ cannot be eliminated from the equations!)

Again, if $Y = R^4 \equiv$ Minkowski space-time, we can write:

$$\vec{E} = -\frac{\partial}{\partial t} \lrcorner D_\theta \theta \tag{13.8}$$

$$\vec{B} = D_\theta \theta - \vec{E} \tag{13.9}$$

These are the "electric" and "magnetic" components of the field. They are $\mathscr{L}$-valued, time-dependent differential forms on R^3.

$$D_\theta \theta = \vec{E} * dt + \vec{B}$$

$$*D_\theta \theta = (*\vec{E}) \pm (*\vec{B}) \wedge dt$$

The *zero energy* solutions of the Yang-Mills field are those for which

$$D_\theta \theta = 0 \quad . \tag{13.10}$$

The "instantons" are those which (possibly after complexification) are given as follows

$$*D_\theta \theta = \lambda D_\theta \theta \tag{13.11}$$

with $\lambda \in \mathbb{C}$.

As mentioned earlier, both of these equations are to be considered as "zero-soliton" phenomena. Before speaking of "solitons" that truly generalize what has been found in two-dimensions (Korteweg-de Vries, Sine-Gordon, etc.) it will be necessary to find a set of "higher" conservation laws which are "in involution" *or* a Bäcklund transformation (the two are probably related). Of course, in going to a general manifold Y we have made the "zero-soliton" problem itself very interesting (it is essentially trivial for Korteweg-de Vries and Sine-Gordon), particularly *geometrically*. (13.10), of course, says that the "connection" determined by θ is *flat*. The geometrical interpretation of (13.11) has just been found (at least for four-dimensional manifolds with constant curvature Riemannian metrics) by Atiyah and Ward. (I plan to cover this in a later volume of this series.) What they essentially show is that these equations can be "prolonged" (more or less in the Estabrook-Wahlquist sense) to certain equations on the manifold $P_3(\mathbb{C})$ (complex projective space of three complex variables) which *can* be classified using sophisticated and complicated algebraic geometry. One may at least hope that understanding the common geometric mechanism underlying the Estabrook-Wahlquist and Atiyah-Ward construction will provide new insights and methods into further classes of important nonlinear partial differential equations.

Now, I want to analyze in detail the most elementary example of this phenomena, the zero-energy solutions of Yang-Mills, but considered *globally*.

Appendix G

THE ZERO-ENERGY YANG-MILLS STATES CONSIDERED FROM THE POINT OF VIEW OF "GLOBAL" DIFFERENTIAL GEOMETRY

Of course, "global" interpretation requires a "global" setting for Yang-Mills. I will now describe one which seems appropriate.

1. YANG-MILLS FIELDS AS CONNECTIONS IN PRINCIPAL FIBER BUNDLES

Let G be a compact Lie group. A *principal fiber bundle with* G *as structure group and with the manifold* Y *as base* is defined by the following data:

a) Manifolds X and Y

b) An onto submersion mapping $: X \to Y$

c) A transformation group action of G on X which is *free* (i.e., $gx = x$ for some $x \in X$, $g \in G \Rightarrow g =$ identity) and such that

The orbits of G are the fibers of π.

Let $\mathcal{G}$ be the Lie algebra of G. The action of G on X gives, infinitesimally, an action of G by vector fields on X; this we denote by

$$\rho\colon \mathcal{G} \to \mathcal{V}(X)$$

for $A \in \mathcal{G}$

$\rho(A)$ = infinitesimal generator of the group $t \to \exp(tA)$ acting on X .

In other words,

$\rho(A)(x)$ = tangent vector to the curve $t \to \exp(tA)(x)$ at $t = 0$.

Since G acts freely, so does $\mathcal{G}$, i.e.,

$\rho(A)(x) = 0$ for some $x \in X$ implies $A = 0$

$\rho(\mathcal{G})(x)$ fills up the tangent space to the fiber π through the point x.

Recall that $\mathscr{D}^r(X,\mathscr{G})$ denotes the $\mathscr{G}$-valued, r-differential forms on X. Thus, a $\theta \in \mathscr{D}^1(X,\mathscr{G})$ is a map

$$\theta\colon T(X) \to \mathscr{G}$$

which is linear on the fibers of the tangent bundle $T(X)$.

Definition. A *connection* for the principal bundle (X,Y,π,G) is a G-valued one-form θ on X satisfying the following conditions:

$$\theta(\rho(A)(x)) = A \tag{1.1}$$

for each $A \in G$.

For $g \in G$, $A \in \mathscr{G}$, $v \in T(X)$

$$\text{Ad } g(\theta(v)) = \theta(g_*(v)) \quad , \tag{1.2}$$

i.e., θ intertwines the action of G, $T(X)$, and $\mathscr{G}$.

Let us see how these conditions define an Ehresmann connection in the usual sense. For each $x \in X$, set

$$H_x = \{v \in X_x : \theta(x) = 0\} \tag{1.3}$$

Our assumptions imply that:

X_x is a direct sum of H_x and $\rho(\mathscr{G})x \equiv$ tangent space to $\pi^{-1}(\pi(x))$.

Thus, $x \to H_x$ defines a field of "horizontal" spaces for the fiber space (π,X,Y), i.e., an *Ehresmann connection*. (See "Interdisciplinary Mathematics", Volumes 10, 12, and 14.) Further, condition (1.3) assures that the Ehresmann connection $x \to H_x$ is *invariant under the action of* G, i.e.,

$$g_*(H_x) = H_{\ell x} \quad .$$

The horizontal vectors can also be defined by a Pfaffian system. Let A_a, $1 \leq a,b \leq n$, be a basis for G. Then,

$$\theta = \theta^a \otimes A_a \quad , \tag{1.4}$$

where θ^a is a set of scalar-valued one-forms on X. Condition (1.1) means that

$$\theta^a(\rho(A_b)) = \delta^a_b \quad . \tag{1.5}$$

H is defined by the Pfaffian equations

$$\theta^a = 0 \tag{1.6}$$

The *horizontal curves* are those curves $t \to x(t)$ such that

$$\theta\left(\frac{dx}{dt}\right) = 0$$

or

$$\theta^a\left(\frac{dx}{dt}\right) = 0 \quad .$$

Let C^c_{ab} be the structure constants of the Lie algebra $\mathscr{L}$, i.e.,

$$[A_a, A_b] = C^c_{ab} A_c \quad . \tag{1.7}$$

Theorem 1.1. The Ehresmann connection defined by (1.3) is flat, i.e., the free vector fields of H are completely integrable (in the Frobenius sense) if and only if

$$d\theta^a - \frac{1}{2} C^a_{bc} \theta^b \wedge \theta^c = 0 \tag{1.8}$$

Proof. As for any Pfaffian system, "complete integrability" means that there are relations of the form

$$d\theta^a = \theta^a_b \wedge \theta^b \tag{1.9}$$

where θ^a_b are some set of one-forms. Clearly, (1.8) implies (1.9). What we must show is that (1.5) and (1.9) imply (1.8).

Condition (1.3) means (in its infinitesimal version) that

$$\mathscr{L}_{\rho(A_a)}(\theta^b) \otimes A_b + \theta^b \otimes [A_a, A_b] = 0 \tag{1.10}$$

where $\mathscr{L}_{(\ )}(\ )$ denotes Lie derivative of a differential form by a vector field. Now, using (1.9),

$$\mathscr{L}_{\rho(A_a)}(\theta^b) = \rho(A_a) \lrcorner d\theta^b + d(\rho(A_a) \lrcorner \theta^b)$$

$$= \rho(A_a) \lrcorner (\theta^b_c \wedge \theta^c)$$

$$= \theta^b_c(\rho(A_a))\theta^c - \theta^b_a \quad . \tag{1.11}$$

Combine (1.9) and (1.10):

$$\theta^b_a = \theta^b_c(\rho(A_a))\theta^c + C^b_{ac}\theta^c \qquad (1.12)$$

Hence,

$$\theta^b_a(\rho(A_d)) = \theta^b_d(\rho(A_a)) + C^b_{ac}$$

or

$$\theta^b_a(\rho(A_c)) - \theta^b_c(\rho(A_a)) = + C^b_{ac} \qquad (1.13)$$

Substitute (1.12) back into (1.9):

$$d\theta^a = (\theta^a_c(\rho(A_b))\theta^c + C^a_{bc}\theta^c) \wedge \theta^b$$

$$= (\tfrac{1}{2}(\theta^a_c(\rho(A_b)) - \theta^a_b(\rho(A_c)) + C^a_{bc}))\theta^c \wedge \theta^b$$

$=$, using (1.13),

$$(+\tfrac{1}{2} C^a_{cb} + C^a_{bc})\theta^c \wedge \theta^b$$

$$= \frac{1}{2} C^a_{bc}\ \theta^b \wedge \theta^c$$

This finishes the proof of Theorem 1.1.

We can also write (1.8) in a way that is independent of the basis chosen for $\mathcal{G}$.

$$\theta = \theta^a \otimes A_a$$

$$[\theta,\theta] \equiv (\theta^a \wedge \theta^b) \otimes [A_a, A_b]$$

$$= (\theta^a \wedge \theta^b) \otimes C^c_{ab}A_c$$

$$= (C^c_{ab}\theta^a \wedge \theta^b) \otimes A_c$$

$$d\theta \equiv d\theta^a \otimes A_a$$

$$D_\theta\theta \equiv d\theta + \frac{1}{2}[\theta,\theta] \qquad (1.14)$$

(As we have already seen, $D_\theta\theta$ is interpretable geometrically as the "covariant derivative relative to the connection θ".) Thus, condition (1.8), i.e., the flatness of the Ehresmann connection, means that

$$\boxed{D_\theta \theta = 0} \quad . \tag{1.15}$$

These equations also have an independent existence in Lie theory; they are the *Cartan-Maurer equations*.

2. THE CARTAN-MAURER EQUATIONS OF LIE GROUP THEORY

So far, $\mathcal{G}$ could have been an abstract Lie algebra--the group G it generates has not played an essential role. It is in the geometric interpretation of the "flatness" condition (1.15) for an Ehresmann-principal fiber bundle connection that puts G into the picture in a strong way--particularly for the physicists.

There are two ways to think about a finite dimensional Lie algebra $\mathcal{G}$, either "abstractly" as a finite dimensional vector space with a bracket operator [,] satisfying certain postulates, or as the *set of left-invariant vector fields on a Lie group* G. It is this latter point of view in which we are now interested.

Suppose that (A_a), $1 \leq a,b \leq n$, is a basis of $\mathcal{G}$, considered as left-invariant vector fields on G. Let (ω^a) be the dual basis of left-invariant one-forms, i.e.,

$$\omega^a(A_b) \equiv A_b \lrcorner\, \omega^a = \delta^a_b \quad . \tag{2.1}$$

The ω^a are called the *Cartan-Maurer forms*.

<u>Remark</u>. Often it is easier to define the Cartan-Maurer forms independently. Presumably, it is for this reason that Cartan himself always preferred to work with differential forms rather than with vector fields. For example, for

$$G = GL(n,R) \equiv \text{group of } n\times n \text{ real matrices of nonzero determinant,}$$

if

$$g = (g^i_j) \quad , \qquad 1 \leq i,j \leq n \quad ,$$

then

$$\omega^i_j = (g^{-1})^i_k\, dg^k_j$$

are those left-invariant forms. To obtain them for the other "classical" groups (e.g., orthogonal, symplectic, etc.), we have only to restrict these forms to the subgroup, and choose an independent set. For example, for $O(n,R)$, the

$$\omega^i_j \quad , \qquad 1 \leq i,j \leq n$$

are the Cartan-Maurer forms.

Now, return to the general Cartan-Maurer forms defined by formula (2.1)

$$\begin{aligned}
d\omega^a(A_b,A_c) &= (A_b \lrcorner\, d\omega^a)(A_c) \\
&= \mathcal{L}_{A_b}(\omega^a)(A_c) \\
&= A_b(\omega^a(A_c)) - \omega^a([A_b,A_c]) \\
&= -\,\omega^a([A_b,A_c]) \\
&= -\,\omega^a C^d_{bc} A_d \\
&= \boxed{-\,C^a_{bc}}
\end{aligned}$$

These equations now imply the following ones:

$$\boxed{d\omega^a = -\frac{1}{2} C^a_{bc}\, \omega^b \wedge \omega^c} \quad . \tag{2.2}$$

or

$$d\omega + \frac{1}{2}[\omega,\omega] = 0 \quad . \tag{2.3}$$

These are the Cartan-Maurer equations themselves.

3. LIE FOLIATIONS. THE SPACE OF ALL DISCRETE FLAT CONNECTIONS IN THE CASE OF A SIMPLY CONNECTED BASE SPACE

Continue with $(X,Y,\pi,\theta,G,\mathcal{G})$ as before. Suppose that the connection defined by the $\mathcal{G}$-valued one-form θ is *flat*, i.e.,

$$d_\theta \theta \equiv d\theta + \frac{1}{2}[\theta,\theta] = 0 \tag{3.1}$$

Let $\omega \equiv \omega^a \otimes A_a$ be *the* Cartan-Maurer form. Since θ and ω satisfy the same Cartan-Maurer equations (2.3) and (3.1), we can look for a map

$$\phi: U \rightarrow G$$

between an open subset U of X and G such that

$$\phi^*(\omega^a) = \theta^a \quad . \tag{3.2}$$

Theorem 3.1. A map $\phi: U \rightarrow G$ satisfying (3.2) is a submersion. The fibers are the submanifolds which are *horizontal* with respect to the Ehresmann connection.

Proof. To say that ϕ is a submersion is to say that $\phi_*: T(U) \rightarrow T(G)$ is onto. Dually, it says that ϕ^* is one-one. This follows from (3.2), since the connection forms θ^a are linearly independent at every point of X. (This can be traced back to the hypothesis that G acts *freely* on X.)

Since the equations

$$\theta^a = 0 \tag{3.3}$$

characterize the horizontal vectors, and since a vector $v \in T(U)$ such that

$$\phi_*(v) = 0 \quad ,$$

i.e., v is tangent to the fibers of ϕ, also (via (3.2)) satisfies

$$\theta^a(v) = 0 \tag{3.4}$$

we see that, indeed, the fibers of ϕ are horizontal.

Here is another way of looking at this result in terms of the theory of *foliations*. The connection form θ defines the *horizontal vector system* $x \rightarrow H_x$ (also called a "distribution" in Chevalley's sense). The flatness of the connection is equivalent to *complete integrability* of the vector field system. It then defines a *foliation* of X be submanifolds. (Each leaf of the foliation in a submanifold $\alpha: Z \rightarrow X$ with $\dim Z = \dim Y \equiv \dim(G\backslash X)$ such that $\alpha_*(Z_z) = H_{\alpha(z)}$, for all $z \in Z$, and such that α is "maximal" with respect to this property.)

A *quotient map* for the foliation is a submersion map

$$\alpha: U \rightarrow X \tag{3.5}$$

from an open subset $U \subset X$ to a manifold Z. (Such quotient maps exist locally--the Frobenius complete integrability theorem--but not necessarily globally. The condition that it exist globally is precisely that the space of all leaves be a manifold; this possibility is discussed in Palais' work [ ]; after twenty years this must still be considered as the definitive word on this question!

This particular foliation is a *Lie foliation* (with G as structure group) in the sense that the $\mathcal{G}$-valued one form θ determines the foliation. Thus, we see the possibility of choosing ϕ so *that* Z *is an open subset of the Lie group* G.

If the base manifold Y is simply connected, and if the Ehresmann connection is *horizontally complete* (see IM, Volume 10) in the sense that curves in Y can be *globally* lifted to horizontal curves in X, then we can say a good deal more. Let L be a leaf of the horizontal foliation. It is readily seen that

$$\pi: L \to Y$$

is a *covering map*, hence is a diffeomorphism since Y is simply connected. Construct a map

$$G \times L \to X$$

by assigning

$$g\ell \quad ,$$

the transform of ℓ by g, to each $\ell \in L$. It is readily seen that this is a diffeomorphism. This explicitly exhibits the fiber space

$$\pi: X \to Y$$

as a *product*, enabling the decomposition map $\phi: X \to G$ to be constructed *globally*. In other words, assign

$$x \to (\phi(x), \pi(x))$$

this is the isomorphism of the fiber space with the product

$$G \times X \quad .$$

We can sum up as follows.

Theorem 3.2. If Y is simply connected, the space of all "zero-energy states" of Yang-Mills fields is identified with the space of all principal G-bundles over Y which are isomorphic to products.

4. THE GAUGE GROUP ACTING ON THE SPACE OF ALL PRINCIPAL BUNDLES AND YANG-MILLS FIELDS

Continue with G as a Lie group and Y as a manifold. The *gauge group* is the space of all mappings

$$\alpha: Y \to G$$

denoted as $\mathcal{M}(Y,G)$. Make $\mathcal{M}(Y,G)$ into a group as follows:

$$(\alpha_1\alpha_2)(y) = \alpha_1(g)\alpha_2(g) \quad .$$

Let $\mathcal{P}(Y,G)$ be the space of all principal G-bundles with base space Y. $\mathcal{M}(Y,G)$ acts--*as a transformation group*--on $\mathcal{P}(Y,G)$ in the following way. An element of $\mathcal{P}(Y,G)$ is a set (X,G,π), where X is a space, together with a free action of G on X and a fiber space mapping $\pi: X \to Y$ whose fibers are the orbits of G. Let $\alpha \in \mathcal{M}(Y,G)$ transform (X,G,π) into (X',G',π') as follows:

$$X = X' ; \qquad \pi = \pi' \quad .$$

G' is isomorphic to G, *but acts as the transformation group on* X *differently:*

$$\boxed{\begin{array}{l} g \text{ applied to } x \text{ is} \\ \alpha(\pi(x))g\alpha(\pi(x))^{-1}x \end{array}} \tag{4.1}$$

The map

$$\beta_\alpha: X \to \alpha(\pi(x))x \tag{4.2}$$

of $X \to X$ is then a bundle isomorphism between the original bundle and the transformed one. In fact, the rule (4.1) is just that required, so that the map (4.2)--which is just what physicists call a "gauge transformation"--*intertwines the action of* G.

The gauge transformation (4.2) also induces an isomorphism on *connections*. Thus, if a *Yang-Mills field* is defined as a pair

(bundle, G-connection)

the gauge group $\mathcal{M}(Y,G)$ *acts* as a *transformation group on the space of Yang-Mills field.*

If Y is simply connected (and if we restrict attention to horizontally complete connections) $\mathcal{M}(Y,G)$ acts *transitively* and *freely* in the "ground states", i.e., the space of *flat connections.*

If Y is not simply connected, proceed as follows. Let $\underset{\sim}{Y}$ be the simply connected covering space to Y. There is then a projection

$$\underset{\sim}{Y} \to Y \quad . \tag{4.3}$$

The "space" of all Yang-Mills fields living on Y can be "lifted up" to be a subset of the space of Yang-Mills fields living on $\underset{\sim}{Y}$. In other words, we have a one-one map

$$(\mathcal{Y} - \mathcal{M} \text{ on } Y) \to (\mathcal{Y} - \mathcal{M} \text{ on } \underset{\sim}{Y})$$

The map (4.3) (which is a principal fiber bundle with structure group $\pi_1(Y)$, the fundamental group of Y) maps

$$\mathcal{M}(\underset{\sim}{Y}, G) \to \mathcal{M}(Y, G) \quad .$$

$\pi_1(Y)$ acts on $\mathcal{M}(\underset{\sim}{Y}, G)$ and on $(\mathcal{Y} - \mathcal{M} \text{ on } \underset{\sim}{Y})$. Thus, the study of Yang-Mills fields on Y reduces to the study of the action of the fundamental group of Y on Yang-Mills fields on $\underset{\sim}{Y}$. (If the connection is flat, then there is a homomorphism $\pi_1(Y) \to G$ determined by holonomy. For the study of the "ground state" Yang-Mills everything would essentially reduce to this assignment

$$(\text{flat connection}) \to (\text{discrete subgroup of } G)$$

I do not want to go into details here. I do not yet know if this is important physically--but I suspect it is.